THINKING "INFORMATICALLY"

THINKING "INFORMATICALLY"

A New Understanding of Information, Communication, and Technology

Antony Bryant

The Edwin Mellen Press
Lewiston•Queenston•Lampeter

Library of Congress Cataloging-in-Publication Data

Bryant, Antony.
  Thinking "informatically" : a new understanding of information, communication, and
technology / Antony Bryant.
      p. cm.
  Includes bibliographical references and index.
  ISBN-13: 978-0-7734-5704-1
  ISBN-10: 0-7734-5704-6
  I. Title.

hors série.

A CIP catalog record for this book is available from the British Library.

Front cover illustration: Reproduced by kind permission of PRIVATE EYE magazine / T Reeve

Copyright © 2006 Antony Bryant

          The Edwin Mellen Press   The Edwin Mellen Press
                  Box 450   Box 67
          Lewiston, New York   Queenston, Ontario
          USA 14092-0450   CANADA L0S 1L0

                      The Edwin Mellen Press, Ltd.
                      Lampeter, Ceredigion, Wales
                      UNITED KINGDOM SA48 8LT

                  Printed in the United States of America

TABLE OF CONTENTS

LIST OF TABLES/FIGURES

PREFACE

I have just finished reading Antony Bryant's book. This remarkable study ends with an appeal: it is high time for 'the far-reaching scope of informatics', stifled as it has been thus far by a variety of self-imposed 'limiting concepts', to emerge 'in its own right' from its semi-tolerated hiding and/or semi-legal confinement 'within the IS academy'. High time, in other words, to acknowledge countless social connections – the roots as well as repercussions – of informatics; and to admit that the advent of informatics both reflects and prompts a chain of crucial social departures: and so it calls for a close scrutiny and radical revision of the ways we think of the world we inhabit - the world which we cannot but shape and re-shape through our interactions. This is the substance of the Author's message – and he makes a very strong case indeed for the message to be listened to and absorbed. Few readers of this book would doubt its soundness and urgency.

I said that I have just finished reading the book. This is not the whole truth, however. I'll surely return to it on many occasions, as it contains the richest source of knowledge I came across of the short, yet meandering and turbulent history of our collective understanding, struggling to catch up with the as yet untapped potential and probable though as yet unanticipated consequences of the information explosion.[i] His book will surely serve for many years as an essential reference – and not just for the experts in informatics, but any scholar keen to penetrate the secret of our still not fully understood world, that while being composed of purposeful human undertakings manages to behave after the pattern of purpose-less and motive-less nature. This book calling us to 'think informatically' is itself a treasure-house of information making such thinking conceivable – and promising to assist us in our efforts to re-assimilate and re-

---

i Paul Virilio writes of the 'information bomb', whose power to change the rules of the survival game far transcends in his view the devastating might of the nuclear bombs.

conquer the world drifting out of our collective control and individual comprehension.

What set Antony Bryant on his voyage of exploration and discovery was the conclusion he drew from the thorough and comprehensive discussion of the apparently easy to understand, perhaps even self-evident, concept of information. This term, Bryant concluded, 'cannot be understood in the context of computer technology without an understanding of what is involved in *communication.*' 'Communication' being a profoundly inter-human affair, an integral aspect of human interaction. This finding suggests that the realm of computer technology is much too narrow a territory in which to seek (let alone to find) the meaning of 'information'; that sociology, as the study of human interaction, is not 'another approach' to the study of information, but its integral, undetachable part and indispensable condition of its success.

From the voyage now completed, Bryant is bringing home priceless trophies: strategic principles and precepts that are capable of making that success feasible. Like: 'We have to begin to understand the specific nature of the "biological, social, linguistic and cultural changes" to which our attention is drawn as the source, nature and limitations of technicism and the full extent and complexities of informatics become apparent'. Or: 'Information is not a "mystical fluid" distilled from the raw data: Communication is not a process of flow from active transmitter to passive receiver: Technology is not an off-limits, asocial form of magic that drives society along once it is widely used'. And finally: 'Informatics has a profound and promising basis, but only once each of the three terms' (information, communication and technology) is 'seen as essentially contested and profoundly social'.

Such assertions may sound heretical in a field serving thus far as a fertile plantation, and then a playground of updated versions of old fetishisms that used to alienate and reify, as a supra-human logics, what in its core is a perpetually innovative human action. The great merit of Bryant's argument is to show, and to demonstrate beyond reasonable doubt, that as long as they go on sounding heretical the chances of an informatics equal to its task are not encouraging, and the odds militating against its facing up to the challenges ahead are overwhelming.

How important it is to all of us, the academics as much as the intended beneficiaries of their studies, to listen carefully to Bryant's argument and to his call, we can gather from just one example: the potential impact of the 'internet fetishism' (an expression coined by Jodi Dean[ii]) on contemporary political life, and particularly on democratic politics. The 'internet fetishism', in Dean's words, 'protects a fantasy of unity, wholeness or order, compensating in advance for their impossibility'. 'The technology acting in our stead actually enables us to remain politically passive ... The "fix" lets us think that all we need is to universalize a particular technology, and then we will have a democratic or reconciled social order'. Theorizing of the internet as the new and improved form of politics, of world-wide-web surfing as a new and more effective form of political engagement, and of the accelerated connection to the internet and rising speed of surfing as advances in democracy, look suspiciously like ideological glosses on the ever more common life practices of the knowledge-class, and above all on their keen concern with an honourable discharge from the 'politics of the real'.

All the more resounding for that reason is Jodi Dean's blunt verdict that the present day communication technologies are 'profoundly depoliticizing', that 'communication functions fetishistically today as a disavowal of a more fundamental political disempowerment or castration', and that

> the technological fetish is "political"... enabling us to go about
> the rest of our lives relieved of the guilt that we might not be doing our
> part and secure in the belief that we are after all informed, engaged
> citizens... We don't have to assume political responsibility
> because...the technology is doing it for us... (It) lets us think that all

---

ii See her 'Communicative Capitalism: Circulation and the Foreclosure of Politics', in *Cultural Politics,* March 2005, pp. 51-73.

we need is to universalize a particular technology and then we will have a democratic or reconciled social order.

Social realities of our time stand in stark opposition to the sanguine and cheerful portrait painted by the 'communication fetishists'. The powerful flow of information is not a confluence of the river of democracy, but an insatiable intake intercepting its contents and channelling them away into magnificently huge, yet stale and stagnant artificial lakes: The more powerful the flow, the greater the threat of the river-bed drying up.

The planetary servers store information, so that the new (increasingly global) liquid-modern culture can substitute forgetting for learning as its major driving force; and they suck in and store the imprints of dissent and protest, so that liquid-modern politics can roll on unaffected and unabated, substituting soundbites and photo opportunities for confrontation and argument. The currents flowing away from the river are not easily reversed and returned to the riverbed: Bush and Blair could go to war under false pretences not for the *dearth* of websites calling their bluff.

As far as the 'real politics' is concerned, on its way towards electronic warehouses dissent is sterilized, defused and made irrelevant. Those who stir waters in the storage lakes may congratulate themselves for their fitness-testifying verve and sprightliness, yet those in the corridors of real power would hardly be forced to pay attention and could be only grateful for the state-of-the-art communication technology for siphoning off their potential troubles and dismantling the barricades erected on their way before such troubles had time to settle. Real politics and 'electronic politics' seem to run in opposite directions, and the distance between them seems to grow as the self-sufficiency of each benefits from the absence of the other's company. The age of simulacra did not cancel the difference between genuine stuff and its electronic equivalents/substitutes, between real and virtual realities; it only dug a precipice between them - virtually easy, but in reality increasingly difficult, to bridge.

This is but one example of the intense two-way traffic between the world and the 'world-wide web', which the emergent discipline of Informatics may ignore not only at its own peril, but to all our loss – the people simultaneously on the acting and the receiving side of the communicative revolution. It is but one of the numerous cases of misconceptions which a narrowly circumscribed and unduly tapered study of the forces behind that revolution and of its many impacts may produce; with grave consequences for the direction our shared life may take when equipped with the tools of electronic communication. Last though most certainly not least, it is but one example of the services which Antony Bryant's timely reminders, convincing arguments and perfectly aimed signposts may render, if given proper attention.

Zygmunt Bauman
Professor Emeritus University of Leeds

FOREWORD

The spread of computer and communication technologies (ICTs) over the past 50 years or so has been remarkable. They affect practically all aspects of our lives, enabling us to do things which in previous ages would have been unthinkable. They have become ubiquitous. Nevertheless their spread has been far from uniform, and the so called digital divide has become a significant problem and source for discussion. Nor are all the consequences from the deployment of ICT universally beneficial.

As might be expected the diffusion of such a significant technology has been paralleled by a growth in regarding the technology, its applications and impacts as a domain of study: at one level because of the need to teach those who work with ICT, but at another more profound level to try to understand the phenomenon in its societal context. In part, it is hoped this study will provide the methods which enable us to make the best possible use of the technology, in part to provide the criteria, practical as well ethical, on what constitutes 'best possible' use, and in part to be able to foresee the consequences on society, on organizations and on individuals of its pervasive spread.

Today this domain of study, under a variety of names, is one of the major divisions in the academic calendar in Universities and Business Schools. Its Journals and Conferences flourish. But it is a domain in crisis. Its legitimacy as a separate field of study has been questioned. Student recruitment in the developed world, after many years of sustained growth has fallen sharply. At the same time a divide has grown between practitioners and academic scholars. An ICT professional walking into a workshop on the role of the actant in Actor Network Theory or the importance of nomological nets would retreat in bewilderment.

Ever since the first schools were set up in academia in the middle and late 1960s scholars have discussed and debated the nature of their subject matter, its boundaries and its relationship with other established academic disciplines. What is clear is that whilst there was common ground on some of the issues that were to be studied, there was little consensus on either the main thrust or the appropriate research methods. The argument on where the studies should focus has divided the community between those who would place the main emphasis on the technology, or the artefact as its advocates term it – the intensive definition[i] – as against those who make the information system itself in its wider context the focus – the extensive definition. A third school[ii] considers that ICT studies need to focus on the work place.

As a response to the current crisis and attack on the domain from outside the debate has sharpened, bringing out much more clearly than before the epistemological and ontological assumptions underlying the differing outlooks of ICT scholars. But the debate has been carried out without acrimony and in the best spirit of academic endeavour.[iii] Nevertheless much of the debate has a defensive tone - partly a debate amongst the community, but partly in defence against the critics from outside the community.

In this book Antony Bryant analyses the way the scholarly community has defined the subject matter. He concludes, following Zygmunt Bauman's analysis of another discipline, sociology, that the discourse on the discipline of Information Systems is flawed. Each element of the ICT triad: Information; Communication; Technology is examined in turn. The way the meaning of these words has evolved is traced, and the confusion and contradictions in definitions are exposed, and some of the myths and misunderstandings which have accumulated in the 50 year history of the domain highlighted.

---

i Land, F. F., 'The Information Systems Domain', in Galliers, R.D., (ed.), *Information Systems Research: Issues, Methods and Practical Guidelines* , Blackwell Scientific, Oxford, 1992
ii Alter, S., 'The Work System Method for Understanding Information Systems and Information System Research', *Communications of the AIS*, 9(6), pp. 90-104, September, 2002
iii King, J.S. and Lyytinen, K. (eds.), *Information Systems: The State of the Field*, Wiley, New York, to be published 2006

As an example of myths, Bryant refers to Boland's characterisation (Boland, 1987) of five fantasies stemming from the way the information is thought of in the ICT community. To these we can add a sixth fantasy, the tacit and dangerous assumption underlying much of the discussion on information and knowledge management, that information as depicted in our systems represents the *truth*. The idea that information and knowledge may be manipulated in an instrumental way is often forgotten, despite the evidence all around us of spin, propaganda, deceit and fraud.[iv]

Bryant discusses the way the ICT community has attempted to define information and dismisses the naïve view that information is processed data. Another approach is not to regard information as a single concept but to classify information according to the intended purpose and properties of different information classes. Land and Kennedy-McGregor[v] distinguish between 'descriptive information' which attempts to provide an accurate and objective description of the real world of people, object, rules and norms; and 'statistical information' which also attempts to describe aspects of the real world, but relies on inferences from imperfect data or models the real world on assumptions of statistical behaviour. They term a third class 'evaluative information' which is more judgemental and subjective. An ICT makes use of each type of information, but often designers and users are unaware of the properties of the information in the system.

If the book ended with its discussion of the current debate and its analysis of the definition of each constituent of ICT it would make a valuable contribution to the debate. But the book goes beyond mere criticism of a flawed discipline. Antony Bryant is optimistic. From his analysis and drawing on a wide range of

---

iv Land, F.F., Nolas, M-S., Amjad, U.Q., 'Theoretical and Practical Aspects of Knowledge Management: Broadening the View', in Schwartz, D.G., (ed.), *Encyclopaedia on Knowledge Management*, Ideas Group, 2005

v Land, F.F. and Kennedy-McGregor, M., 'Information and Information Systems: Concepts and Perspectives', in Galliers, R.D. (ed.), *Information Analysis: Zelected Readings*, Addison Wesley, Sydney, 1987 sources he concludes that we need to rethink where the discipline fits in, and by *thinking informatically* revitalise the domain, and its position in relation to related disciplines in the social sciences. He suggests that the discipline has a future as a central discipline amongst its peers.

This book is provocative and important. It is essential reading for scholars and students in the social sciences. It lifts discussions on the topic to a higher plane and provides the framework for a bright future.

Frank Land
Emeritus Professor in the Department of Information Systems
London School of Economics

ACKNOWLEDGEMENTS

This book could not even have been contemplated, let alone completed without the encouragement and support of my wife, Griselda Pollock. I have also been enormously fortunate to have been able to benefit from the enthusiastic support and insight of Zygmunt Bauman and Frank Land – each one an authority in his respective field, and each also retaining the passion and fervour of the true scholar.

INTRODUCTION

This is a book with grandiose claims: An attempt to re-orient a discipline – perhaps more than one – by scrutinizing existing disciplinary claims and offering in their place a glimpse of a wider, richer but more inchoate series of starting points. The embryonic discipline in question currently goes by a number of different names – management information systems [MIS][1], information systems [IS], information management [IM] are just three of the most widely used – and has been marked both by spectacular growth and continued crises of identity since its inception. The growth has been of three distinct kinds; growth in resources, growth in technological range and scope; growth in conceptual reach and ambit (see chapter 6). These three forms have led in different directions at different times since the 1950s, giving each specific era its own flavour of identity crisis; but there is a general similarity and continuity to these crises as will be explained in the chapters that follow.

At the heart of the discipline there lies the development of computer-based information systems [CBIS] beginning in the late 1950s. By the middle to late 1960s CBIS issues were sufficiently coherent in an academic sense that in the USA, under the rubric of MIS, there were academic appointments, specific under-graduate and post-graduate courses, and researchers in place. In North America MIS departments were mostly spawned within Business Schools, Departments of Management and the like. In many European countries the equivalent groups tended to emerge from within Computer Science Departments, and so from their very inception there was at least a dual character to IS/MIS.

In his recent contribution to a symposium for one of the founding figures of MIS, Mason (2005) traces the emergence of MIS in the US. He lays stress on the *systems* nature of the discipline, and argues that its emergence was impelled

---

1 This introduction uses several overlapping and competing terms – MIS, IS, IT, ICT etc. – the differences and similarities will be explored in detail in chapter 1.

by a variety of influences from existing disciplines including management studies, operational research [OR], and systems analysis.

It is critical to note that all of these reference or bedrock disciplines predated the appearance of the commercial computer – but were indelibly marked by its emergence. So although many key issues in MIS were not novel to the field, they took on new meaning and consequence as a result of the appearance of commercial computing in the 1950s.

Although some texts inexplicably omit or ignore it, the first genuinely viable and effective commercial computer system was developed in the UK for J. Lyons & Co: LEO, the Lyons Electronic Office, in 1951. Mason uses 1954 as his 'pivotal year', with the installation of a UNIVAC machine to process payroll for General Electric. He also notes that the 1950s saw the formation of institutions oriented specifically to systems approaches; notably the Society for General Systems Research. The age of commercial computing gathered pace in line with a general tendency for technological acceleration and increasing complexity and inter-relatedness. As usual the hard, technical and operational reality was well in advance of conceptual and intellectual developments that might help in its understanding.

The period from the 1960s to the late 1970s witnessed the ways in which computers began to 'shock' the organization, as Gibson and Nolan pointed out in their work on technological maturity (see Nolan, 1982). In fact there was not a single, short-sharp-shock but rather a series of shocks as part of a process of profound change and disquiet as computer technology moved from highly specialized and somewhat constrained applications to far wider accessibility and implementability. Whatever the strengths and weaknesses of this particular concept of maturity, it did at least draw attention to the reality of technological innovation on a large scale as more than simply *plug-and-play*; or even plug-and-pay. Stafford Beer encapsulated both the challenge and the threat of the new context the question which asks how to use the computer in the enterprise, is, in short, the wrong question. A better formulation is to ask how the enterprise should be run given that computers exist. The best version of all is the question asking, *what, given computers, the enterprise now is.* (Beer, 1981, stress in original)

If early computer technology shocked the organization, the appearance of the PC shocked everyone, with further jolts and surprises from the internet, mobile communications and so on. Beer's challenge now has to be extended to reach beyond organizational confines – so we might now state it in somewhat Yoda-like[2] terms as *what, given ICT, society now is?*

So whatever one's view of the actual nature of the changes from 1951 to 2001, after 50 years of the commercial computer age the field of studies focused on CBIS has to contend with a vast range of rapidly changing technologies and artefacts, and a widening impact of those technologies on an ever-increasing range of human social activities.

A key consequence of this has been that whatever constituted the field of MIS or IS, many parts of it are now up for grabs by sociologists, psychologists, cultural theorists, economists, and virtually anyone who has a claim to be responding to the question *what, given ICT, society now is?* Certainly the technical issues remain important, but relative to social and cultural aspects of ICT they are taking a diminished role.

Consequently by the early years of the 21st century we are witnessing the end of the spectacular growth of MIS/IS as an academic field. The identity crisis that has been ever present since the 1950s can no longer be attributed to adolescence and a growth spurt. It may well be that we are in danger of passing

---

2 Yoda being the sagacious Jedi Master from *Start Wars* whose wisdom does not extend to following generally accepted sentence construction – see http://en.wikipedia.org/wiki/Yoda

straight through to senility and obsolescence. The crisis of identity is acute as the gee-whiz factor disappears; or is taken up elsewhere, or becomes a generic social feature (see chapter 5). The decline also has an impact on funding. In the UK for instance computer-related undergraduate courses now attract the same level of government support per student as do other undergraduate courses, whereas previously the former had attracted a premium of around 50%. In part this is justified on the basis that all students now use and require computer support.

This is exacerbated as the impact of out-sourcing, off-shoring and general familiarity with the technology undermines the market power of IS/IT graduates, which reduces the demand for such courses, with ramifications for the status and employability of orthodox-MIS academics. Just as we marvel at the paucity of the $3000 PC of the early 1980s compared to what is now readily available for half that figure – and a fractional amount in real terms; so too organizations and people are re-evaluating what they are prepared to pay for basic IT skills, and wondering why they ever needed to pay so much for so little only 10-15 years previously.

The message at the heart of what follows is that if MIS – well actually informatics (see chapter 1) – is to avoid the leap from adolescence directly to senility then we must make a start on the project of re-orienting ourselves. Mason argues that a 'loosely knit field of inquiry becomes a tightly woven discipline when it acquires four things'; one of the four is 'theories and concepts'. One of the problems with MIS as it currently exists is that its central concepts are themselves in need of clarification and remedy, both in the light of changes in the entire context of the field and weaknesses in the concepts themselves. The chapters that follow offer a starting point for this, and seek to justify and motivate a new collective conceptual and intellectual project termed *informatics*. This will require a deep and critical analysis of three core and defining concepts; *information* (chapter 2), *communication*(s) (chapter 3) and *technology* (chapter 4). It will also demand an engagement with other disciplines, and an enhanced understanding of the economic, social and environmental context of the 21st

century (chapter 5). The move will result in a wider, less cohesive but more challenging and encompassing discipline of informatics.

This project is not new in itself. As long ago as 1987 Boland argued that the central concept of MIS – information – remains elusive, and that 'we as researchers have failed to address the essence of information in our work'. He highlighted what he termed the five *information fantasies* – pointing out that fantasies 'have two faces: a productively imaginative one, and an erroneous, self-deluding one' (1987, p367). Unfortunately, as Boland acknowledged in 1987, the first face has proved considerably weaker than the second; an imbalance that has if anything got even more marked in the last 20 years. With reference to the five fantasies, ICT is seen to focus around (1) structured, disembodied data; (2) managed in a narrowly defined rationalist manner in hierarchical, command-and-control organizations; (3) with little attention paid to issues of power and difference; (4) with a view of intelligence that ignores its creative, interpretive nature; (5) and where *more* information is automatically assumed to mean *better*, with an ultimate aim of perfect information.

What is required is that we challenge each and every one of these five, and that we also extend this scrutiny to the concepts of *communication(s)* and *technology*. Bauman (Bauman & May, 2001) has called for us to start *Thinking Sociologically*, and I wish to supplement and extend this with an exhortation to start *thinking informatically*. Haraway (1985) has offered a definition of informatics as the 'technologies of information as well as the biological, social, linguistic and cultural changes that initiate, accompany and complicate their development'. I will argue that this needs a slight revision to include 'technologies of information and communication'; and that we can then develop a way of thinking that seeks to understand these technologies and their ramifications, and that also 'opens up the possibility for thinking about the world in different ways' (Bauman & May, 2001, p5).

Again paraphrasing Beer's position; the question which asks 'what is MIS?' is, in short, the wrong question. A better formulation is to ask how MIS needs to be changed given the current social and technological context. The best version of all is the question asking, *what, given ICT, **informatics** now is?* And in what follows I hope to be able to offer a persuasive argument for devoting our energies to *thinking informatically.*

PART ONE
INFORMATICS

CHAPTER 1
THINKING INFORMATICALLY

'Only a discipline flawed as a discourse has to offer an apology, feels the need to justify its right to exist. ... Concern with self-justification has been, since the beginning, a conspicuous feature of *infological* discourse.' (Bauman, 1992, p76)

The original version of this quote uses the word *sociological* rather than the ugly but evocative term *infological*. The ideas that Bauman expresses and the argument he develops are, however, at least as appropriate and useful when applied to the *infological* context as they are to the sociological. Before proceeding to justify this claim, the use of the term *infological* needs some explanation; which will lead to its replacement by a less uncomfortable one.

Imagine the scene in a surreal edition of *Who Wants to Be a Millionaire?* The hapless contestant is faced with the question – 'What is the correct term for the study of the use and application of information and communication technologies?' – Is it a) Information Systems[3]; b) Information Management; c) Information Technology; or d) Informatics?

If the contestant wishes to *phone a friend*, who will be chosen? Will it be someone from a university that offers a programme in Information Technology, or where the faculty or school itself is called Information Technology? Or will it be someone from a different university that has opted for Information Systems or Information Management for broadly identical entities? What if they phone

---

3 I have opted for the term IS as opposed to MIS – Management Information Systems; the latter prevails in North America. The two are largely synonymous, although MIS might be seen as subset of IS since the latter has a broader compass. However, as will be seen later, the two share some crucial ambiguities.

someone conversant with the work of Donna Haraway (1985) who defines informatics as the 'technologies of information as well as the biological, social, linguistic and cultural changes that initiate, accompany and complicate their development'? Unlike the world of quiz programmes, there is no correct answer. We can either tender our own suggestion or make a choice from those on offer, although we do not do so in conditions of our own choosing.

The choice made here is the term defined by Haraway, but amended to read as follows; the study of 'technologies of information *and communication* as well as the biological, social, linguistic and cultural changes that initiate, accompany and complicate their development'. What follows can be seen as the extended justification for this choice.

There may be some objection to the term *informatics*. It is something of a clumsy neologism, like sociology, but the alternatives are riddled with ambiguity and are even more objectionable and conceptually far less robust. *Information technology* [IT] simply will not do, although it is probably the most commonly used term amongst non-specialists. But IT is both conceptually and linguistically problematic. Linguistically information *technology* is bound up with the hardware, and perhaps with the software – what some highly influential writers have termed the 'IT artifact' (Orlikowski & Iacono, 2001); but that is where it begins and ends. This might be seen as a sufficient and satisfactory constraint and foundation. Indeed a recent paper in the house journal of the gatekeepers of the discipline, *MIS Quarterly*, specifically argued that the discipline has to develop a clearly identifiable core, explicitly avoiding what the authors term errors of *inclusion* and *exclusion* (Benbasat & Zmud, 2003). (The authors of the article were concerned with what they term the *IS* discipline – but this confusion of terms will be dealt with below.)

Even if IT is expanded into ICT [Communications] this is still to remain within the realm of the actual artefacts, the things you can kick, rather than the sorts of concern that Haraway draws to our attention with her definition. Moreover the use of IT or ICT to refer to the *study* of the technology, rather than the technology itself, is to add to the confusion. It might be pointed out that use of the term *History* suffers from the same ambiguity, although the context usually resolves this; but there might be contexts in which 'The End of History' is a threat to people's academic jobs rather than a provocative title for a book or article.[4] Historians and others seem reconciled or oblivious to this potential ambiguity. For a newly emerging discipline such uncertainty is debilitating: So much for IT/ICT.

Information Systems [IS] is perhaps a better candidate, although there is still the problem of confusing the process of study with the object of study – a criticism which applies equally to MIS, the preferred acronym in North America. The recent document outlining the curriculum for undergraduate degree programs in IS perpetuates this confusion since it offers guidelines for the curriculum aimed at students 'majoring in information systems' (i.e. the process of study), but also states that 'Information Systems are complex systems' (i.e. the object of study).

Markus (1999) has suggested using the term *Academic* IS in referring to the discipline. In this way the academic field of study 'is clearly differentiated [both] from the subject of the study and from the functional unit in computer-using organizations'. This seeks to distinguish between not two but three concepts, since there is now the further distinction between the object of study (the information system in general) and the functional unit (the component or characteristic of an organization). These latter two can be confused because the term IS can be understood to refer to the generic topic, concerned with the ways in which technologies centring on communication and sharing of information can be developed and utilized effectively in various – predominantly organizational – contexts; and also to refer to the unit within an organization that is responsible for the development, maintenance and availability of those technologies and

---

4 At the time of first writing this section, the UK Secretary of State for Education – Charles Clarke – was embroiled in a controversy over his remarks which could be seen to be the start of just such a policy; and in UK universities the 'end of chemistry' is also potentially on the agenda.

infrastructures. In most contexts this distinction is not problematic, although in universities it is always likely to be a source of confusion. If someone works in 'Information Systems' in a university are they primarily involved in teaching students, or in running the university's information system?

In contrast to both of these, Markus wants to stress that her concern is the academic discipline, including the study of both the generic subject and the specific functional context. So for IS, just as with the term IT, there is the need to uncouple the processes of analysis and study from the subject or focus of this analysis. Failure to do this simply adds a further source of confusion to an already bemusing domain of over-lapping acronyms – IT, IS, ICT; and contested terms such as *information, technology, communication.*[5] Unfortunately the term *Academic IS* is somewhat cumbersome, and the term IS is all too easily confused with IT. Markus' argument, however, is well founded, even if the net result of Markus' argument is not satisfactory. Indeed Markus demonstrates this same confusion and simultaneously undermines her earlier argument in concluding her essay with a plea for a new start 'so that we can create the IT (sic) field of the future!' (p202).[6]

The recent report detailing ideas for 'A Framework for Information System Concepts' [FRISCO] opens with the statement

> When talking about the information system area, different people may have different views about how broad or narrow this area is, and which other scientific disciplines are related to this area, and in which way.

> Even the term 'information system' itself is interpreted quite differently by different groups of people. It seems to be interpreted in at least three different ways:

---

5 See chapters 2-4

6 The term Academic IS might itself be misunderstood and thought to apply to the functional unit within universities – so there is further reason to drop the term altogether; although it will be used in a different context in chapter 6.

As a technical system, implemented with computer and telecommunications technology.

As a social system, such as an organisation[7] in connection with its information needs.

As a conceptual system (i.e. an abstraction of either of the above).

(Extract from FRISCO report, 2001 revised edition, section 1.1 – including the footnote below relating to the definition of 'organization'.)

The FRISCO authors do not explain who these 'different groups' might be; but the clear point is that the term itself is problematic and open to wide and inconsistent misinterpretation. Again our hypothetical quiz contestant would receive an unhelpful response if he chose to *ask the audience* made up of representatives of the different groups identified above.

What about the term Information Management [IM]? This is a far more useful and inclusive term since it represents a move away from a focus on the technology – **IT/ICT** – towards a concern with the information itself. (This is not to argue for a complete decoupling of IT from IM.) This is somewhat akin to the distinction between automotive engineering and transport management. The former is far more seductive, with an array of glossy monthly magazines devoted to the latest developments in cars, bikes etc. – but ultimately if people are going to be able to use these machines there has to be some analysis and management of traffic, transport policies, infrastructure and so on. Similarly with IT/ICT, again there are the glossy monthlies, but there also has to be the study of how everything fits together and actually works on a practical basis and in a sustained

---

7 The term 'organisation' is used here and throughout the report in the most general sense. Not only large companies are meant. One-man companies, profit- and non-profit-oriented organisations, clusters of companies interacting in some way, universities and research institutes are meant as well. Even the community of all Internet users and similar communities may be considered organisations.

and robust manner. This is not to argue that technical and engineering issues are not important or profound, but it is to point to a range of key issues beyond the distinctly technically-focused ones. In this regard IM is a useful term, but it still does not provide the breadth and depth that is required; it is best used as the term that refers to the practice of managing information, as opposed to managing the information technology, and so it is necessarily narrower and more sharply focused than any concept that should refer to the more disparate field of study.

Thus with some considerable authorial sleight of hand, we are left with *informatics*. Perhaps a somewhat unwieldy term, but one that does allow us to distinguish between the study and the object(s) of study; and one that, using and revising Haraway's definition, clearly encompasses a full and wide area of concern. Furthermore the word itself, although seemingly originating in English, actually has a wider resonance in other languages.[8]

So the case can be made for the use of the term *informatics* – even though it clearly leads to Benbasat & Zmud's *errors of inclusion* (see below). Yet even those who might object to the term itself would probably agree with the characterization of what it means. Certainly if the term is to be anything more than a convenient label it must have a more substantive set of claims. Before developing these, however, we need to establish the opening point that informatics is, in Bauman's terms, a discipline that is 'flawed as a discourse'.

To paraphrase Bauman yet again, it can be argued that informatics discourse was 'brought into being by the encounter between the awesome task of the management of organizational processes on a grand, *corporate and* societal scale and the ambitions of the modern state *and corporation*' (original – applied to sociological discourse – some terms added in italics – Bauman, 1992, p76).

---

8 Thus French, German, and Italian/Spanish all have equivalent terms – respectively *informatique, informatik, informatica*. Portuguese and Korean use the term informatics, and Chinese and Japanese also have an equivalent word. The specific meaning of the term in different languages will almost certainly not align with the definition argued for here. Moreover to add to the confusion, current usage in both English and French sometimes equates informatics with computer science.

Bauman notes that the outcome of this encounter between management and social ambition was the articulation of a 'collection of engineering *problems*'. In similar fashion, and in part deriving from the same impetus, the technology and its accompanying conceptual apparatus arrived as a set of engineered solutions. This reinforces the point made by Weizenbaum amongst others, who have argued that information technology came 'ready made' into the context that demanded its use; 'the remaking of the world in the image of the computer started long before there were any electronic computers' (Weizenbaum, 1984).

But this is not the feature that makes informatics into a flawed discourse. The problem arises because informatics, or whatever label is applied, has no autonomy from other discourses; and in this sense it is similar to sociology. Drawing on the work of Foucault, Bauman demonstrates that disciplines cannot be defined in terms of what might appear to be the 'obvious' aspects such as 'permanence of a thematic' or 'a well-defined alphabet of notions'; but, following Foucault, must be seen as *discursive formations*.

> 'We sought the unity of discourse in the objects themselves,
> in their distribution, in the interplay of their differences, in their
> proximity or distance – in short, in what is given to the speaking
> subject; and in the end, we are sent back to a setting-up of relations
> that characterizes discursive practice itself; and what we discover is
> neither a configuration, nor a form, but a group of *rules* that are
> immanent in a practice' – Foucault quoted in Bauman, 1992, p69

From this perspective any discipline must be seen to constitute its topic and its practices. As Bauman argues it is not a case of reality waiting to be portrayed by 'its court painter'. In other words there is no pre-existing corner of reality waiting to be claimed and explained by a specific discipline; nor is the discursive formation a 'disturbing element' which superimposes itself upon some 'pure, neutral, atemporal, silent form'. The 'incessant activity of discourse ...

spawns the narrated reality at one end and the narrating reason at the other' (Bauman, 1992, p70).

Furthermore this 'narrating' is not something that can be ascribed to specific individuals but has to be located and grounded within institutional sites 'from which this discourse derives its legitimate source and point of application' (quoted in Bauman, 1992, p70). Foucault makes the point very explicitly with reference to insanity, psychopathology and medicine. Thus the institutional sites from which medical expertise is dispensed, from which it 'derives its legitimate source and point of application' (quoted in Bauman, 1992, p51), are those associated with hospitals and the generic medical infrastructure. Similar institutional issues apply to the IS discipline as it currently exists; and the prime dispensaries include, but are not restricted to, institutions such as *MIS Quarterly* [*MISQ*], *IS Research* [*ISR*] and the Association for Information Systems – all predominantly albeit not exclusively North American.

It must be noted that although I have argued for the term *informatics* as the most appropriate for 'the study of the use and application of information and communication technologies', I am not denying the existence of a 'discipline' best referred to as IS (despite the points made earlier about the actual confusion of the term IS itself). This 'established' discipline can be seen to exist in Bauman's terms as a 'flawed discourse' continually seeking to spawn a narrated reality and to articulate a narrating reason. For the remainder of this discussion I shall continue to use the term IS to refer to this disciplinary formation, contrasting it with the more tenuous – but conceptually more profound – disciplinary claims for informatics. The relationship between the two might best be envisaged as one whereby the more long-lived and established – but constrained – IS is gradually spawning a more far-reaching and intense informatics; which ultimately must seek to encourage and promote similar tendencies in other disciplines.

A discipline may be announced with all manner of fanfare and flourish, and may even be instigated in some institutional fashion; but for any discipline to claim and sustain its own identity it has to establish and maintain its autonomy with regard to other discourses – drawing and defending its boundaries. In this respect disciplines vary in their ability and propensity to maintain their distinctive character and boundaries. For many esoteric sciences this is not a primary issue since the boundary may be widely, if sometimes grudgingly, acknowledged.[9] Bauman points to physics as a discipline where such self-delineation is exemplified; although he also uses the example of political statements under totalitarian regimes as another –

> ... non-specialists would not challenge the statements of the physicists for lack of access to the events which they narrate; the subjects of an authoritarian government would not contest political pronunciations for lack of access to data guarded by official secrets acts. (Bauman, 1992, p72)

He adds that in most cases 'the two factors intertwine'; echoing the ideas of Feyerabend (1993) who likened the operation of scientific disciplines to organized crime gangs. And there is also a resonance with Foucault's concept of a discipline – knowledge conjoined with power – incorporating both the concept of a branch of learning and a form of control and punishment with various sanctions against non-compliance.

Furthermore disciplines such as physics and astronomy share a monopoly not only of experiences but also of equipment – usually expensive and complicated. As such, scrutiny of their findings can only easily be carried out by others equally immersed in the discipline, and with similar access to the means to investigate.

But this is a privileged position for any discipline, and one not enjoyed by sociology, which cannot stake any monopolistic claim to 'objects and events already construed and pre-interpreted within other social discourses'. Indeed

---

9 In fact acknowledgement of boundaries does not usually have to be 'wide', but does have to be clearly acknowledged by those other disciplines most closely related. This is a particular problem for informatics. There is no corner of a foreign field that is forever informatics!

Bauman argues that sociologists cannot even claim superiority in such interpretations, since we, as social actors and observers, all have access to precisely the 'objects and events' at the centre of sociological analysis.

The IS discipline as it now exists exemplifies Bauman's and Foucault's observations regarding the nature of such discursive formations and their potential crises of identity and imperfections as a discourse. There has been an incessant stream of articles, books, conferences and so on focusing on the *identity* of the discipline. There are endless boundary disputes over endless boundaries, and even fundamental concepts such as *information* are lacking in any consensual definition. In addition, the ubiquity of the technology has resulted in extensive familiarization both in an everyday manner and on the part of rival disciplines; so that increasingly any claims to specialism and superiority on the part of those at the centre of the discipline, or who consider themselves to be so located, are open to challenge or undermined completely. Technology is truly quotidian.

Demonstrating Bauman's point about a flawed discourse having to offer an apology for its identity and existence, the principal institutional centres of existing IS have continued to wrestle with the issues of identity and demarcation. The key institutional sites 'from which this discourse derives its legitimate source and point of application' are fairly easily identified – even if there is considerable debate about the meaning of their pronouncements. The two key journals are *MIS Quarterly* and *IS Research*. *MISQ* has repeatedly engaged with the issue of the identity of IS, and its relationship to other disciplines; and the 2003 edition of the *Communications of the Association of Information Systems (CAIS)* contained more than a dozen articles on the topic; many in response to Benbasat & Zmud.

The *MISQ* 2003 issue featured an article by Benbasat & Zmud (2003) – both senior figures within the institutional sites of IS, and both past editors of *MISQ*. They argue that the IS scholarly community has, from its emergence in the 1970s, sought to 'develop a meaningful, resilient identity within the institutions that comprise its organizational field – namely the organizational science and information science research communities, business and information science academic institutions, and the various organizations, industries, and professional groups that comprise the information technology (IT) industry.' Acknowledging that after 30 years 'insufficient progress has been made', the authors are keen to provide a basis upon which a meaningful, resilient identity can be built.

They begin, promisingly if confusingly, by characterizing IS scholars as 'a community of nascent entrepreneurs attempting to create a new population, i.e., the IS discipline'. This appears to echo Foucault's idea of a socially mediated discourse or discursive practice; but why the use of the term 'population' rather than 'institution'? (And why use the term *entrepreneurs*?) This is made immediately apparent since the authors have derived the term from the work of Aldrich who was writing about *organizational* development; where the idea of an organization as a population seems appropriate. Aldrich grounds this process of creation of a new population in two forms of legitimacy – 'cognitive' and 'sociopolitical'. The latter bears some resemblance to the issues elucidated far more provocatively and imaginatively by Bauman, following Foucault, since it refers to 'acceptance by key stakeholders, the general public, key opinion leaders, and government officials of a new venture as appropriate and right'. But this is of only minor concern to Benbasat & Zmud; they are far more worried about cognitive legitimacy – leading to 'acceptance of a new kind of venture as a *taken for granted* feature in the environment' (stress in quote as it appears in Benbasat & Zmud, 2003).

They assert that 'the IS discipline has made significant progress' with respect to 'sociopolitical' legitimacy,

> as seen via the institutionalization of IT as an integral part of today's organizational and economic contexts, the acknowledgement of the importance of IS by academic accreditation bodies, the presence of IS academic departments and the degree programs ..., a professional society (Association for Information Systems) ..., and the aforementioned respect afforded to *MIS Quarterly* and *Information Systems Research*.

But for Benbasat & Zmud this is not sufficient, they yearn for cognitive legitimacy and conceptual unanimity; precisely the unity of discourse based on a 'well-defined alphabet' or 'permanence of a thematic' that Foucault and Bauman characterize as an elusive and impossible objective. Benbasat & Zmud specifically state that their aim is to articulate 'An Identity for the IS Discipline'. Almost as if they have read Bauman, and are seeking to offer a mirror image of his argument, they claim that a 'natural ensemble of entities, structures, and processes does exist that serves to bind together the IS subdisciplines and to communicate the distinctive nature of the IS discipline to those in its organizational field – the IT artifact and its *immediate* nomological net.' (stress in original).[10]

Since no specific definition is offered of the term *nomological net*, it must be assumed that it is largely another way of stating that the IT artefact exists, and so too does this 'natural ensemble of entities'. What comprises this ensemble is indicated in a diagram with accompanying text. The authors explain that their view of what constitutes the approved and legitimate purview of IS consists of striving to understand

> (1) how IT artifacts[11] are conceived, constructed, and implemented, (2) how IT artifacts are used, supported, and evolved, and (3) how IT artifacts impact (and are impacted by) the contexts in which they are embedded

---

10 The fascination with 'The IT artifact' can be traced back to a key article by Orlikowski & Iacono (2001) in the other house journal of the IS gate-keepers – *IS Research*. It should be noted that although the phrase seems redolent of those who always want to stay conceptually close to the stuff you can kick, raising the issue of the IT artefact is an attempt to get researchers to 'take technology seriously'. On the other hand this topic has taken a new turn with the paper by Carr (2003) the editor of *Harvard Business Review* in May 2003, provocatively entitled 'IT Doesn't Matter'.

11 Where the word is used within a quote from elsewhere, the original US spelling of artefact has been retained.

This seems at least minimally in keeping with our amended characterization of informatics; but Benbasat & Zmud clearly wish to constrain the interpretation of their set of core properties to a 'managerial, methodological' view of the world. Thus they stress that the nomological net is to be thrown around only those constructs that are *'intimately* related to the IT artifact'. To clarify this view they point to what they term *errors of inclusion* and *errors of exclusion* with regard to articles that have been previously published in *MISQ*. Their main reason for doing so is that such errors lead to ambiguity in the 'boundaries of IS scholarship'. Their tacit, but clear message is that flagship publications such as *MISQ* should be the site of unambiguous delineation of the discipline's identity and reinforcement of the discipline's boundary.

In offering this view of the discipline and its governance, Benbasat & Zmud are continuing a discussion that has beset IS since its inception, but which has grown in intensity particularly in the US in the past few years as the existence and budgets for IS departments in universities have come under attack.

However much IS-purists such as Benbasat & Zmud might try to defend some mythic *core* of the discipline[12], there is a necessary and inevitable engagement with a whole variety of other disciplines, which leads to profound problems of identity and demarcation. IS is a 'flawed discourse'. The boundaries between it and other discourses are fuzzy – indistinct to the point of disappearance; and the topics at the centre of the discourse are claimed not only by other discourses but by everyday 'commonsense'. Indeed, with the ubiquity of the technology and the terminology, these claims have actually increased to the extent that in 1999 Markus could ask 'What Happens if the IS Field as We Know it Goes Away?'

Markus was not arguing that the field will actually disappear in the sense that 'Horse & Buggy' studies might have disappeared – or certainly declined – had it ever existed in the 19th century academy. On the contrary, the threat is not

---

12 Although for them it is not a mythic core, but a very real one.

one of disappearance but of dissipation and dissolution. 'As computers increasingly become embedded in every aspect of personal and organizational life, it is less and less possible to distinguish between computing and *everything else.*' (1999, p176) The unthinkable, as Markus puts it, is that the IS disciplinary turf will be cut up and hauled away by a host of other disciplines. 'We bemoan the fact that intellectual communities like organizational behaviour, operations management, and marketing are *discovering* information technology (IT) as an important topic for *their* teaching and research. ... we see them as laying claim to research domains that we think of as ours.' (1999, p175). (At this point I leave it to the reader to decide who is included in and excluded from the 'we', 'ours', and 'them' to which Markus refers.)

Her evidence to support the claim for endangerment of Academic IS is that – at least in the USA – resources aimed specifically at Academic IS are under effective attack from other parts of the academy. Significantly fewer posts are being allocated to this domain, the justification being that the same requirements can be met with hiring 'IT-knowledgeable non-IS faculty'. This trend might be reversed if there is a large and continuing demand for Academic IS itself – but that begs the question of what constitutes the domain as such. In order to answer this question Markus develops her argument initially by examining the ramifications of a customer-based justification for Academic IS. Thus, like Benbasat & Zmud, Markus is arguing from an embattled position that aims to defend the disciplinary turf of IS from a range of predators in rival areas. This is not just a conceptual issue, it relates to jobs, budgets, research grants and other concerns understandably close to the heart of all academics.

The customer-based argument uses the parlance and procedures of business planning and applies them to the academic endeavour, in order to identify 'the *customer* and the *core mission* of Academic IS teaching, research and practice' (1999, p178). Markus notes that the general assumption has been that the key customers are 'organizations that use computers', but this is problematic or certainly too simplistic since it fails to differentiate between *user*-organizations (i.e. where IT/IS products and services are consumed) and *producer*-organizations (i.e. where IT/IS products and services are developed to be sold on to others) – the latter growing in importance as outsourcing has developed and grown more pervasive.

In order to develop her argument Markus attempts to clarify the mission of Academic IS, not a simple task since it is built upon such disparate foundations. Thus those who would characterize the mission as developing 'useful computing applications (software) efficiently and effectively' (quoted by Markus, 1999, p179), offer far too dated and limited a view; while those who consider aspects such as management,[13] rather than technical development can find themselves having to fight their corner against the technical people on one side and the business and management specialists on the other. (It should not come as a surprise that there seems to be no clear way of making a mission statement, since apart from Star Trek's *The Starship Enterprise*, when did mission statements ever make much sense?)

Markus' response to this doubly unsatisfactory, but perhaps largely self-inflicted, state of affairs is to widen the scope of Academic IS considerably, both in terms of customers and mission. In order to overcome any disagreeable implications of her argument, which seems to be leading to a product without a unique selling point, she offers an alternative view of Academic IS as the 'electronic integration of socio-economic activity'[14]. With tongue firmly in cheek, she adds her 'personal contribution to the terminological turmoil', expanding IT as '*Integration Teknowledgy*, where *integration* is shorthand for *electronic integration of socio-economic activity* and *teknowledgy* is my term for *knowledge and skill in the area of electronic content, information, communication, technologies and systems*' (1999, p197). Although falling short, this does seem to be heading in the direction of Haraway. Unfortunately, however, Markus leaves

---

13 Whether this is management of IT, IS or Information is not stated.

14 Hardly the slogan for an effective marketing campaign.

her readers with a perplexing coda, since she concludes by calling for jettisoning the Academic IS field of the past 'so that we can create the IT (sic) field of the future!' – the slogan severely underselling the product.

This undermines the whole tenor of her argument about the distinction between IT, IS, Academic IS and the like; simultaneously committing the error of *inclusion*. Her six forms of integration seem to cover a vast range of issues, crossing into other disciplines and simultaneously blurring the boundaries between them. Again we have an indication that here is a flawed discipline, constantly needing to justify its existence, with indistinct boundaries that are unrecognized and challenged by rivals, and with central 'objects and events already construed and pre-interpreted within other social discourses'. Both Benbasat & Zmud, in a fairly positive tone, and Markus, with a potentially pessimistic one, are responding to a perpetual crisis of identity.

Following the logic of Bauman's argument, there is no reason to suppose that the stream of writing that tackles the identity issue for IS will come to some definitive halt. The editor of the *MISQ* issue in which Benbasat & Zmud's article appeared noted that 'I doubt that we will ever achieve unanimity within the information systems discipline about whether we have a serious identity problem within the discipline.' This might look like something akin to a couple arguing over whether or not they are incompatible; but in fact the editor is simply describing the true state of affairs. In contrast to Markus, and Benbasat & Zmud, some are happy to embrace a 'fragmented adhocracy'[15], others argue in favour of diversity, and against any effort to develop and regulate a unifying paradigm. This latter group might point to other disciplines that are in a similar state, but the *MISQ* editor argues that this is no reason to ignore the real concerns.

What we have as the current state of affairs in IS is a paradigm case of a discipline as a flawed *discursive formation*: Constantly engaged in the Sisyphean

---

15 *Adhocracy* – the term in this context seems to have first appeared in Alvin Toffler's *Future Shock* in 1970; it was later used and popularized by Mintzberg (1989) in his writings on organizational forms and strategy.

task of having to justify its existence; fraught with debates on what constitute relevant research topics, and legitimate and valid research methods. Much as some might wish this state of affairs to be brought to an end in some conceptually sound and conclusive fashion, this is not going to occur. On the other hand, the discipline can be seen as an 'incessant activity of discourse' spawning the *narrated reality* and the *narrating reason*; with both emanating from a well-recognized and self-perpetuating group of institutional sites. Thus the editors and key contributors to *MISQ* and IS Research, together with those at the top echelons of the Academy of Information Systems [AIS], IFIP [International Federation for Information Processing], and key funding organizations could seek to impose their view of the *core values and properties* on the discipline through the expedient of supervising – or 'policing' in Foucauldian terms – the avenues of publication, recruitment and research funding. Benbasat & Zmud seem fairly content with the 'sociopolitical' basis for the discipline; and many would agree – albeit from a position of criticism rather than satisfaction – that *MISQ* and IS Research have succeeded in narrowing the range of issues and authors that gain access through these journals.

It might then appear feasible for a series of wide-ranging and coincidental editorial decisions to establish the boundaries and identity of the discipline. Perhaps this is already in train in the aftermath of Benbasat & Zmud's positing a set of core values, and Orlikowski & Iacono's insistence on a focus around the 'IT artifact'? But any such attempt at *closure* is fortunately unlikely to prove effective; and although the IS disciplinary establishment is fairly easy to identify (consisting of real authorities and virtual institutions), it is unlikely to strive – consciously – for such an end.

Moreover any attempt to implement such a strategy will be undermined by the terminology. The authors of the FRISCO report (2001) note that not only is there a varied vocabulary – IT, IS etc. – but that even those who use the same term, often mean different things, and those who 'interpret *information system* in the same way use apparently different sets of concepts to explain it, and they apply a different terminology'. Contributors to *MISQ*, *ISR* etc., students and others will – and should – continue to find comments on their work when they use the terms IT and IS interchangeably or with inadequate foundation. But no-one will be able to offer a definitive, once-and-for-all set of definitions; we can only aim to provide attempts at clarity and coherence.

The foregoing should not be taken to imply that *MISQ & ISR* are total redoubts secured against any alternative or critical voices. The issue in which Benbasat & Zmud's article appears also contains a paper by Lamb & Kling (2003) aiming to 'reconceptualize users as social actors' – with Zmud himself identified as the accepting senior editor. It could be argued that this is squarely within the core properties of IS – a component of the *nomological net*; but this is difficult to sustain after a careful reading of the piece and its bibliographical sources. More critical, however, is the observation that many of the authors of papers in both journals seem to be drawn from a relatively small and specific group; one which excludes many well known figures who publish widely elsewhere. Of course this may be a self-perpetuating state of affairs, with non-like-minded researchers failing to submit their work to these two journals since they have gained a reputation for 'only' publishing 'main-stream' articles.

Bauman observes that the 'predicament of sociological discourse may best be grasped by the Kantian idea of an *aesthetic community* ... a territory defined by agreement inside well-protected boundaries' (1992, p75). A similar predicament confronts the existing IS discourse, for Bauman shows, using the work of Lyotard, that such a community is an illusion.

> The community required as a support for the validity of such judgment [of taste] must always be in the process of doing and undoing itself. The kind of consensus implied by such a process, if there is any consensus at all, is in no way argumentative but is rather allusive and elusive ... This kind of consensus is definitely nothing but a cloud of community. (quoted in Bauman, 1992, p75)

In his later writings Bauman claims that all communities are illusory; but here Bauman concludes that sociological discourse is truly constituted by the Sisyphean objective of seeking to establish and sustain a 'real community'; yet if ever it managed to achieve this goal, it would mark the death knell of the discourse: So too for IS and for informatics.

This means that although efforts such as those of Benbasat & Zmud, Markus, and Orlikowski & Iacono are ultimately doomed; they are also ineluctable and must be awaited and answered. In so doing there is the necessity to develop critical thought in Foucault's sense of 'the endeavour to know how and to what extent it might be possible to think differently, instead of legitimizing what is already known' (quoted in Bauman, 1992, p83) – what Rorty promotes as *abnormal discourse*. The proposal to consider the full implications of the term *informatics* is precisely an effort to bolster this abnormal discourse.

What might this abnormal discourse look like? And what is the *normal* discourse that it seeks to challenge? Again Bauman offers a basis for understanding this in the infological context from his perspective on the sociological. As has already been noted, Bauman locates the emergence of the sociological with the outcome of the encounter between the ambitions of the modern state and the 'awesome task of the management of social processes'. This led to a discipline characterized by an 'engineering-reformatory-managerial' edge; one which saw itself at least as much beholden to practitioners as to the academy. This is immediately applicable to the existing IS discipline, which has a constant yearning for 'relevance' in precisely this sense of reference to the practitioners.

This has become a clearly articulated key issue following Westfall's paper of 1997 entitled 'An IS Research Relevance Manifesto'[16]. This states that 'we need to be more relevant to meet the increasing needs of our students, the organizations that hire them, and the larger society.' This is a perfectly laudable aim, even if it again springs from the perceived threat to the IS academic field –

---

16 Note that this US author refers to IS rather than MIS.

'The IS field is shrinking'. Whether the issue of relevance can be addressed across the three constituencies – students, organizations, society – without contradiction is another matter, as is the fixation with IS *Research*; why not locate the source of relevance in the discipline itself, stressing teaching and education?

Bauman notes that early sociology was *monological* (NB nothing to do with *nomological*, although Benbasat & Zmud's outline of core properties seems to emanate from a monological stance), treating its subject matter as a series of objects, to be assessed, measured and regulated. The process of investigation was a *monologue* conducted by the active and articulate researcher with respect to the passive, silent topic of investigation, rather than a *dialogue* between two or more participants. With its origins in computer science and IT, the discipline of IS in its present guise emerged in a similar fashion, and still retains this identity, although now it is increasingly tempered by a dialogic orientation that challenges such assumptions. This owes much to the emergence of several varieties of abnormal discourse, many emanating from within established IS institutions.

In this early phase, informatics in its IS embodiment – like sociology – developed as a series of efforts aimed at ameliorating the introduction of technology into the organizational work place, where it was seen as a prime source of increased efficiency and enhance effectiveness. As such the discipline was largely seen as a method of enquiry derived from a quantitative approach based on empirical methods and measurement.[17]

Using Weber's term, Bauman states that there was an *elective affinity* 'between the scientifically objective ambitions of the rising sociology and its managerial involvement' (1992, p79); a similar but more intense affinity applied to the ambitions of the emerging IS discipline in the 1960s and 1970s – and still pervades many aspects of the IS world.

---

17 And so closely linked to Taylorism and other forms of investigation into work discipline and regulation aimed at enhanced productivity and efficiency.

In a fairly short time, this overwhelmingly monological and behavioural view was challenged; but even now a large part of the IS community – however ethereal that might be – work largely with a view that centres on '*managed social processes* ... that cast social reality as an object of a designed change ... while *disarticulating* all other aspects' (Bauman, 1992, p81). These 'other aspects' include human subjectivity, and asymmetries of influence, power, control and deviation.

The challenges that did arise to this position can be seen in part as impelled by the wave of *post-modernity*. A phenomenon that has swept across all disciplines, and which Bauman describes as a combination of two aspects whereby the political state has retreated from 'programmes of grand social engineering' and where the intellectual faith in 'utopianism' and 'foundationalism' has been undermined. (Bauman teasingly invites the reader to decide which of the two was the initiator. If it was the first, then the intellectual response is just that, a mandated reaction that occurs as a necessary adjunct to a changed situation. If it was the second, then this casts contemporary intellectuals in a more favourable light.)

> Without deciding between the rival claimants, we can still agree that much as there was an intimate link between universal ambitions of legislative powers and the unchallenged domination of legislative reason in philosophical and social-scientific discourses, there is more than coincidence in the simultaneous erosion of the two. (Bauman, 1992, p82)

Bauman sees the impact of this on sociology as turning the two faces of the discipline to face in the same direction. No longer is there the tension between one orientation to the state and another to the individual. The state is no longer a key focus, it has been replaced by an organizational one, in which individuals strive for and seek to sustain their identities. It is as if Mills' *sociological imagination* (1959) has been dismantled and supplanted by the *organizational imagination.* Whereas the former required individuals seemingly to efface themselves, or at least to absent themselves while allowing supra-individual forces free rein – at least at the explanatory and conceptual level; the latter results in a mutual dependency between 'the guardians of mini-orders and the individuals abandoned to the tasks of self-construction' (Bauman, 1992, p89), both having a vested interest in *'managerial services'*. Management and self-management differ in degree, but not in kind; both require 'an *interpretive*, a sense-making, a *world-mapping* knowledge, that results in a mental setting in which decisions are taken and freedom of choice is exercised'.

In some regards Markus seems to be moving along similar lines in noting that the unit of analysis for Academic IS 'sets it apart from other similar fields', since it is concerned with organizations and individuals or groups embedded in organizations. Moreover this organizational orientation has to develop from a purely internally-focused one to an externally-focused one, incorporating inter-organizational processes. This looks promising but Markus' perspective seems far more focused on systems applications – in the computing and IT sense of the term – than it is on organizational processes, and her conception of 'electronic integration of socio-economic activity' is weighted far more to the electronic side than to the socio-economic one: Hence her desire to create the 'IT field of the future'.

Bauman's view is that contemporary sociology 'does not need *protreptics'* (literally an urging on, or persuading – derived from Plato's praise for the Socratic method of instruction), because it is 'resonant with its own structure … a flexible and self-reflective activity of interpretation and re-interpretation'. Informatics as it currently exists is not in the same position, lacking the *fluidity* that Bauman repeatedly invokes in his current writings. Such an objective might be one worth invoking, but at present this is not the future that the disciplinary gate-keepers appear to have in mind. Within existing IS the lessons of post-modernism are still in the process of being understood and evaluated. Judging by the trend of articles in *MISQ* and *ISR*, the 'engineering-reformatory-managerial' flavour still retains its centrality and influence in the discipline; albeit under increasingly vociferous challenges. Those who have sought to articulate this as the rationale for the discipline either end up with an outline for a *legislative* and regulatory basis – Aldrich's 'sociopolitical', but with *disciplinary* overtones; or undermine their own argument with far too wide-ranging a characterization of the discipline.

For the former – such as Benbasat & Zmud – a number of questions are raised, or begged: Who should define the core properties? Who should arbitrate on what counts as 'errors of inclusion' and errors of exclusion'?

For the latter, including some interpretations of Markus' *integration*, and Orlikowksi and Iacono's 'IT artifact', the issue is *what is left out* of their characterization of the discipline?

Markus seems to want to integrate everything with everything; but this seems to be a route to certain oblivion and eventual disappearance. More alarmingly, she specifically expresses the hope that somehow we can all start over, with a clean sheet – but this is exactly what we cannot do. Although it is not a sufficient basis for a discipline, it is still necessary for there to be a 'body of knowledge, and ... certain practices which use this knowledge while simultaneously adding to it' (Bauman & May, 2001, p2). Markus herself seems to understand this when she targets what she terms 'canonical AIS' (p181). She fails to develop this idea or even to give much credence to the idea of a canon of/for the discipline; hence her call for a new start. We might term this a *tabula rasa informatica*, which like all examples of a *tabula rasa* is an interesting assumption or premise, but a cognitive impossibility. Her use of the term 'canonical' is firmly located in and around the technology – the 'IT artifact'. Thus in discussing 'canonical Academic IS' she mentions minicomputers, PCs, office automation, networks and communications systems.

The word *canon* itself is derived from the Greek word for model or standard; but the term is usually understood to have religious connotations, referring to a regulation or dogma of the church, or more specifically to an authoritative list of texts forming The Holy Scriptures. Thus the first canonisation exercise is held to date from the formal selection of what constituted the Hebrew Scriptures, 'made by an emergent priestly caste around the seventh century BCE' (Pollock, 1999, p3). This religious meaning has been displaced, but the term itself appropriated by secular bodies, so that it now refers to a 'displaced religious sense of the sacred text as the beacon of common culture for an educated elite' (LaCapra, quoted in Pollock, p3).

The many and increasing allusions to a list of technologies – 'IT artifacts' – are indicative that the IS canon is perhaps at present literally a list of models or standard forms of technology, presided over by a small and self-selective group of gatekeepers. On the other hand, the wider and far less established informatics canon – in the sense of a set of writings – is in disarray or of questionable status. In this sense it is akin to the canon of Qumran, a collection of manuscripts found in the Judean Desert since the 1940s; a series of individual scrolls, but with no guide to their sequence or associations. The situation is made more contentious by the presence of several extra-canonical works, including parts of what are now termed the *Apocrypha* (texts not included as part of canonical Judaism) and *Pseudepigrapha* (books falsely ascribed to biblical authors). This evokes the image of the 'fragmented adhocracy' alluded to earlier in the context of IS and informatics.

If informatics is to have any claim to be a discipline – and to be distinguished from IS – then, although there is no need for a canon, there must be a generally recognized and elaborated 'body of knowledge' that can be identified and assessed; and continually revised and developed. In many of his writings, Bauman uses the metaphor of *gardening*, evoking the sense of an engagement with natural growth, but one where there is an agenda of control, selectivity and engineering. So too must this be seen to apply to the development of an informatics body of knowledge. The religious control of the canon no longer exists, but as Pollock shows, the canon, although often presented in terms of a naturally emerging order, is in fact the result of a sustained process of selection and discrimination. But this is never totally effective, and leads to the blooming of many different varieties – if not a hundred flowers.[18]

The current IS establishment is remarkably free from the sexual discrimination that prompted Pollock's work; but this is not to say that *everything in the garden is lovely*. On the contrary, there is a profound sense in which many would see the current IS canon – inchoate as it might be – as a North American fiefdom, profoundly positivist and heavily slanted towards neo-liberalism. Fortunately this position has been and continues to be increasingly challenged, both from within and without; but there is still a sense in which the limitations of the normal discourse and even the abnormal discourse need constant re-positioning. Moreover if people are to be encouraged and provoked into *thinking informatically*, then not only must the IS canon be challenged and renewed, but so too must a whole raft of other discourses and their canons.

Informatics is then a discipline constantly having to apologise for itself and continually having to reassert its right to existence – and funding. In fact it is a still, small voice battling under a partial pseudonym of IS. Inside IS is a larger discipline struggling to emerge and develop its own identity; the irony is that neither IS nor informatics will actually be able to do this if the concept of discipline is seen in terms of the erection and defence of boundaries. Following Foucault and Bauman, disciplinary practices have to be seen as fluid projects not as structural and structuring strategies. The task is endless; at its core is not a single, clear objective but an unremitting process of continual explanation, explication and dialogue.

The IS community is truly an imagined one – but some of its members have stronger and more influential imaginations than others. Not all, however, have similar or even consistent/complementary imaginings, hence the constant struggle between the claims for the disciplinary centre ground or bases. Those

---

18 There are several projects aimed at establishing bodies of knowledge [BOK] in areas such as Information Management, Software Engineering, Quality Management, Project Management etc. This book is offered as a contribution to the development of an informatics BOK.

advocating the centrality of concepts such as the IT artefact, nomological nets, and the like have to do battle with those who are equally strident concerning other bases for the discipline, or none at all. The discussion in the wake of Benbasat & Zmud's article is evidence of this conceptual variety. The point is not to pursue some form of conceptual closure but to engage with the flow of argument.

There are no boundaries – although of course in terms of jobs, funds, resources and the like someone, somewhere will make boundaries pay and so some form of disciplinary advocacy is demanded – but this is a very different project from the conceptual one.

Whatever the outcome – however temporary – informatics is essentially permeable, with both a push and a pull to this permeability. The pull can be found in the constant *borrowing* of terms and models from other disciplinary discourses – particularly engineering, but now increasingly also from sociology, semiotics and cultural studies. The push refers to the ways in which terms such as information, IT and the like have become part of common parlance. The push usually comes after the pull, and in some cases the initial borrowing is returned with added richness – sometimes in a confusing fashion as will be seen in chapters 2-4.

With regard to the social and organizational borrowings, there have been influential uses of ideas from Giddens, Habermas, Foucault, Latour and many others. Rather than disparaging or discouraging this, it is essential that it continue. In effect it is part of the rounding out of the disciplinary discourse of informatics into the full definition given earlier.

In recent years the work of Anthony Giddens has been highly influential in the IS academies; particularly his work on structuration[19] (1984). This has been in keeping with a trend that sees the discipline as a social science rather than a

---

19 The concept of structuration is itself derived from Bauman's work, specifically *Culture as Praxis* (1999, originally published in 1973).

technical-managerial one. This characterization has not, however, been readily or universally accepted, and the continuing discussions about 'core properties' and the like indicates an extensive uneasiness about moving too far towards a qualitative social science. Nevertheless it is clear that such a tendency is growing in importance, and if it is to be nurtured as a contending viewpoint then the engagement with or move into the humanities must be taken more seriously. In this case the work of Zygmunt Bauman offers an important basis for such a project. His writings on post-modernity and culture, although not engaging specifically with technology, information and communication, are a key resource in the development of informatics as a discipline.

In the chapters that follow I intend to offer a series of suggestions of ways in which we can begin to *think informatically* – openly and avowedly borrowing from Bauman's work. Before this can be done, however, some extensive *ground clearing* is required, targeted at the three key terms at the heart of the field – however defined – *information, communication* and *technology*.

PART TWO

INFORMATION, COMMUNICATION, TECHNOLOGY

The previous chapter presented a view of informatics as the study of 'technologies of information *and communication* as well as the biological, social, linguistic and cultural changes that initiate, accompany and complicate their development' (Haraway's definition expanded to included communication.) The acronym IT has increasingly been replaced in recent years with ICT, extended in the same way that the technologies for processing information have become increasingly and primarily used with communicative intent. In the next three chapters the three concepts bound together in ICT will be examined separately; since each has a chequered history in its use within an informatics context, and all too often the 'accepted' sense of the term fails to account for many of its key characteristics.

CHAPTER 2

INFORMATION

'What in [information] did Bloom ... admire?'

Its universality: its democratic equality and constancy to its nature in seeking its own level: ... its indisputable hegemony ... its persevering penetrativeness: ... its infallibility as paradigm and paragon: .... its ubiquity: James Joyce, *Ulysses* (original amended, replacing 'water' with 'information')

Every historical period has its godword. There was an Age of Faith, and Age of Reason, an Age of Discovery. Our time has been nominated to be the Age of Information. ... there is another reason for the increasing popularity and generality of the word, one that tells us something important about an era that is willing to accept such a seemingly characterless designation. Unlike 'faith' or 'reason' or 'discovery', information is touched with a comfortably secure, noncommittal connotation. ... It is bland to the core and, for that reason, nicely invulnerable. Information smacks of safe neutrality; it is simple, helpful heaping up of unassailable facts. In that innocent guise, it is the perfect starting point for a technocratic political agenda that wants as little exposure for its objectives as possible. (Roszak, 1986, p32-3)

Information is ubiquitous in the sense that everyone now talks about it and is conscious of it; like the British view of the weather, *there is a lot of it about*: But what is information? Is it one of those terms that has more of an intuitive claim to comprehension than a conceptually specifiable one? Is it akin to concepts such as *time, society, culture* – terms which we all seem to understand until we are asked to define them?

Roszak noted that the concept of The Age of Information had already gained currency by the mid-1980s; and certainly by the early 1990s there was far more attention paid to the term, and hence a plethora of attempts to define and characterize it – whereas previously it was 'nothing to get excited about' (Roszak, 1986, p15).

Table 1 – Definitions of *Information*

Information is …
'knowledge communicated concerning some particular fact, subject, or event' – OED   'only a measure of the difficulty in transmitting the sequences [i.e. messages] produced from some information source' – Shannon & Weaver   'a pattern or design that rearranges data for instrumental purposes' – Daniel Bell   'the result of modeling, formatting, organizing or converting data in a way that increases the level of knowledge for its recipient' – Burch et al   *Examples from Liebenau & Backhouse (1990)*
'Information is data that have been organized and communicated.'   *Porat – quoted by Castells, 1996, p17*
'Information usually implies data that is organized and meaningful to the person receiving it. Data is therefore raw material that is transformed into information by data processing.'   *Davis & Olsen, quoted in Introna, 1997, p49*
'By themselves, data are meaningless; they must be changed to a usable form and placed in a context to have a value. Data become information when they are transformed to communicate meaning or knowledge, ideas or conclusions.'   *Senn quoted in Introna, 1997, p50*

The definitions in Table 1 are all drawn from the IS literature, and as we shall see, give a specific slant to the term. Introna (1997) distinguishes between the information *systems* (IS) concept of information and that of information *science*. For IS 'the only condition for data to become information is that it must be *meaningful to the recipient*' (1997, p50) – stress in original. For information science the concern is that the effect or result of information 'must *change* the recipient; it must lead to a level of interpretation and *understanding*'.

As these examples demonstrate there is no single, authoritative definition of the term; and furthermore there is also no clear focus around which the definitions and characterizations cohere. Introna points to the divergence and discrepancy between the information *systems* view and the information *science* one, but even that is confusing since Introna's distinction between the two is less helpful than might at first sight appear – what is the difference between being 'meaningful to the recipient' and 'changing the recipient' given Introna's view that 'changing' amounts to reaching a different 'level of interpretation and understanding'?

The terms information *systems* and information *studies* themselves have different meanings in different contexts and in different cultures; and the two in no way exhaust all the other fields where *information* is coupled with something else. For example what is the meaning of *information* in contexts evoked or delineated by information *technology*, information *studies*, information *engineering*, and information *management*? And what of the claims made from disciplines as diverse as engineering, semiotics, linguistics, computer science, computing, software engineering, business, management – all of which, in various guises and from various sources, claim the term in some fashion?

Where Introna is correct, however, is the intimation that the term has a range of different meanings, although these are far more numerous and less distinct than he implies. There are multiple claims to the term, and its resonance and importance has changed in the past 50 years so that, far from being dull and humdrum, it must now be considered to be an 'essentially contested concept'.

The idea of an 'essentially contested concept' was first propounded by Gallie, in 1956; specifically with regard to political terms such as 'power' and 'democracy'. Since then the label of 'contested concept' has often been applied to any term which is the subject of substantial disagreement, but Gallie himself offered a set of clear 'minimal criteria' for a concept to be seen as *essentially contested*. The criteria can be explained as follows:-

1. the concept must be 'appraisive in the sense that it signifies or accredits some kind of valued achievement' – i.e. deemed to be significant and valuable;

2. the achievement 'must be of an internally complex character, for all its worth is attributed to it as a whole';

3. this complexity of praiseworthy achievement leads to a variety of descriptions of the nature and process of the achievement;

4. the achievement must be 'open', in the sense that there has been 'considerable modification in the light of changing circumstances' which could not have been predicted;

5. those who use the term must recognize that their specific use 'is contested by those of other parties, ... to use an essentially contested concept means to use it against other uses and to recognize that one's own use of it has to be maintained against other uses.' It has to be used 'aggressively and defensively';

6. there must be some 'original exemplar whose authority is acknowledged by all the contestant users of the concept', failing which there is the risk of 'radical confusion';

7. the continuous competition for acknowledgement should enable the 'original exemplar's achievement to be sustained and/or developed in optimum fashion'. (Gallie, 1956)

So does 'information' satisfy the criteria for being seen as an 'essentially contested concept'? And is it useful to consider the term in this light? To pre-empt what follows, the answers are respectively – 'only partially' and 'yes'.

The term is certainly used 'appraisively', although this is really an effect of its 'open achievement' since, as Roszak has pointed out, until recently (1970s and beyond) information 'was nothing to get excited about'. In fact the ways in which information is an achievement lie at the centre of its being a contested concept, since it is precisely its nature as an achievement that distinguishes those who use what can be termed the 'chemical engineering' metaphor for information, from those who characterize it as a social accomplishment. Gallie's point about 'appraisiveness', however, usefully alerts us to this issue and the deeper implications of the diversity in definition. Thus criteria 1 and 4 are met in part, but not in the sequence that Gallie implies.

Criteria 2 and 3 apply more readily once it is understood that the term does not currently have a specific and single meaning as some of those quoted above seem to imply; although those such as Liebenau & Backhouse (1990), and Introna (1997) are justifiably adamant that no single, authoritative definition now exists. These authors clearly acknowledge a range of contending definitions, and so criterion 5 seems to have been met, except that such authors are arguing against those in the IS discipline who write as if there is no such dissension. As Introna notes, the editors of *The Computer Journal*, published by the British Computer Society, twice sought to devote an entire issue to the subject of 'information', and on both occasions failed to elicit sufficient interest and had to complete the issue with other articles. Criterion 6 is then somewhat ambiguous, since there are those who would acknowledge an original exemplar – within IS this would be something along the lines of 'information is processed data' – but this is precisely what others would contest; while within other disciplines, such as engineering, there would be divergent and contradictory, alternative exemplars. As will be seen later, there are several *original* exemplars – that is the problem. So Gallie's criterion 6 is something of a problem if taken literally – but surely if a concept is 'contested' then that contestation might derive from views of what constitutes its initial statement, as is certainly the case with the term 'information': Alternatively the state of 'radical confusion' might be endemic and ineluctable.

The final criterion is one that cannot be judged at present; if at all. We are still deeply entrenched in a phase of competition and contention, and perhaps Gallie's rationalist and modernist confidence that concepts can ultimately be optimally developed is something that we would now see as impossible and even undesirable. Some might take this to mean that the term 'information' can be used to mean just whatever anyone chooses it to mean – and so concur with the popular view of Lewis Carroll's Humpty Dumpty; '"When I use a word," Humpty Dumpty said, in a rather scornful tone, "it means just what I choose it to mean, neither more nor less."' But those who quote this need to read the full conversation that Alice has with him.

> 'When I use a word,' Humpty Dumpty said, in a rather scornful tone,' it means just what I choose it to mean, neither more nor less.'
>
> 'The question is,' said Alice, 'whether you *can* make words mean so many different things.'
>
> 'The question is,' said Humpty Dumpty, 'which is to be master – that's all.' (Lewis Carroll, *Through the Looking Glass*, chapter 6)

The many contending definitions of 'information' reflect what Bauman might term 'liquid terminology', and it may be that some form of authoritative view will emerge – a master in some sense; although the entire tenor of Bauman's position is that the search for authoritative exemplars is currently – and foreseeably – a forlorn undertaking. But at present it is far more important to ensure that Gallie's criteria 1, 2, 4 and particularly 5 are widely acknowledged to apply. 'Information' as a term is value-laden and appraisive; it does refer to an achievement; there has been considerable modification from its initial meaning;

and those involved in the field of informatics have to understand that their claims to the term are highly contested and must be employed 'aggressively and defensively'. This then has ramifications with regard to the identity of any discipline that centres itself on 'information' – whether this is the IS discipline or informatics in the sense introduced and favoured here.

Introna, and Liebenau & Backhouse offer accounts of the ways in which information has developed in meaning, and the current wide-ranging characterizations of the term. The term itself predates the development of the electronic computer, and dictionary definitions date its origin to the 14th century. The Merriam-Webster Collegiate dictionary gives a range of definitions that include

> - *the communication or reception of knowledge or intelligence*
> - *knowledge obtained from investigation, study, or instruction*
> - *facts, database: the attribute inherent in and communicated by one of two or more alternative sequences or arrangements of something (as nucleotides in DNA or binary digits in a computer program) that produce specific effects*

This encompasses both the idea of information as *facts*, and information as the *communication and/or reception* of facts; but it is only in the 20th century that the term takes on the additional gamut of meanings that make it interesting and problematic. The 'old masters' with whom it is associated in the 1940s are Claude Shannon and Norbert Wiener; so perhaps their definitions of the term could be taken as the 'original exemplars'?

Shannon's name is usually one of the first to be invoked in any discussion of the meaning of the term 'information'. Standard texts on *information theory* (e.g. Usher, 1984) refer to his work as a researcher at AT&T's Bell Labs in the USA in the 1940s and 1950s. His primary interest was the ways in which the capacity of communication channels could be quantified and maximized; specifically with regard to telephone lines. His definition of information can be given as $I = -log\ p$; where p is the probability of an event. The maximum value of p is 1. A value of 1 indicates certainty that the event will occur, a value of 0 indicates certainty that it will not occur. The value of $log\ p$ will be negative so Shannon added a minus sign so that the value of I – the measure of information – will be positive. Shannon's definition of information is posited in terms of the *amount or quantity of information* (1948).

This may appear to be a strange and idiosyncratic view until one understands that AT&T were in the business of maximizing the available technology that linked telephones – in the 1940s a network of copper cables. As an increasing number of phones needed to be linked to the network, it was important to have some basis upon which to decide whether the existing capacity might be exceeded, and hence require upgrading or replacement. Thus Shannon's work was based on the *volume* of information, the *rate* at which it could be transmitted from its source, and the *rate* at which it could be received at its destination – the *flow* of information. Furthermore Shannon was concerned about the *physical* nature of the *channel* that linked source to destination. He noted that a channel could be provided by a 'band of radio frequencies or a beam of light', but he could not have foreseen how important such wire-less technologies would become, and hence the centrality and enduring nature of his work.

By the time Shannon died in 2001, although little known outside his field, the obituaries noted that every time we make a phone call, play a CD or connect to the net we incur a debt to him, because we are using technologies that derive from his pioneering insight into the nature of information and the process of communication.

In fact Shannon's concept of information is very specific and in some regards peculiar and atypical. His focus was on the process of communication originating with an *information source*, and ending with an *information destination*; in between passing through a *transmitter*, then across a *channel* to a *receiver*. Shannon defined the destination as 'the person (or thing) for whom the message is intended' (1948, p2), and by implication the source must be a person (or thing) that sends a message to a specified receiver. Although this appears to include aspects such as meaning, intention, and so on, Shannon was very clear that 'these semantic aspects of communication are irrelevant to the engineering problem'. The key is to focus on the *message* as one *selected* from a set of possible messages.

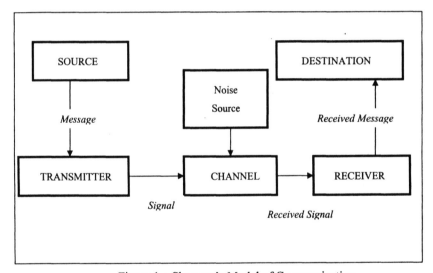

Figure 1 – Shannon's Model of Communication

Anyone seeking to use Shannon's model as a basis for discussions about information and communication must be wary of trying to apply his ideas to *non-engineering* contexts. The most obvious issue is that Shannon explicitly excludes *meaning* from his model. A further problem is that, as Sveiby (1998) has argued, Shannon's model appears to conflict directly with a set of ideas about information derived from the work of his contemporary, Norbert Wiener. Wiener coined the term 'cybernetics' in his book 'Cybernetics: Or Control and Communication in the Animal and the Machine' – also published in 1948. Wiener's concern was to demonstrate how control and communications are linked, and have similar characteristics in both machines and animals. From this he went on to argue that the concepts of *information*, *structure* and *entropy* are related.

> The notion of the amount of information attaches itself very naturally to a classical notion in statistical mechanics: that of entropy. Just as the amount of information in a system is a measure of its degree of organisation, so the entropy of a system is a measure of its degree of disorganisation. (Wiener, quoted in Sveiby)

Systems theorists, amongst others, have developed this idea, linking information to communication, decisions and control. A mechanism or organism – indeed any form of system – uses information to steer towards some predefined goal: The information coming in the form of signals that can be received and compared with some desired level of performance, which introduces the concept of (negative) feedback. Thus information about the actual performance is used to determine what – if any – action needs to be taken to move towards the predefined goal and desired level of performance. (The term cybernetics stems from the Greek word for steersman – *kybernetes*.)

Wiener's idea that information and communication reduce uncertainty, and increase structure does not seem counter intuitive. On the contrary most of us would accept a definition of information that includes a claim that the more information we have, the less uncertain we are. We would possibly also agree that more communication implies more information and more order. (Although we might begin to entertain doubts about *more* being the same as *better*.) Yet this is the exact opposite of Shannon's concept of information; for Shannon information is *the same as* entropy, not its inverse as it is for Wiener.

Katherine Hayles illustrates these conflicting issues relating uncertainty and entropy in the context of information theory with a very useful example which is worth quoting at length.

> Within information theory, information is identified with choices that reduce uncertainty, for example when I choose which book, out of eight on the reading list, my seminar will read for the first week of class. ... Uncertainty enters in another sense as well. Although information is often defined as *reducing* uncertainty, it also *depends* on uncertainty. Suppose, for example, *Gravity's Rainbow* is the only text on the reading list. The probability that I would choose it is 1. If I send an email telling my students that the text for next week is *Gravity's Rainbow*, they will learn nothing they did not already know, and no information is communicated. The most surprising information I could send them would be a string of random letters. ... For an individual message, the information increases as the probability that the event will occur diminishes; the more unlikely the event, the more information it conveys. ... Most of the time, however, electrical engineers are not interested in individual messages but in all the messages that can be produced from a given source. ... Thus Warren Weaver, in his interpretation of Shannon's theory of information, suggested that information should be understood as depending on both predictability and unpredictability, pattern and randomness. (Hayles, 1999, p32)

In other words, for any message to convey information there must be what Hayles terms 'surprisal' – there is no point continually telling me something I already know. If you do, then the information I get will be about you – or your view of me – rather than anything to do with the specific meaning of the message itself. Assuming that there is an element of 'surprisal' in the information, once I have that information then my uncertainty is reduced; this is Wiener's sense of information. If the message was one drawn from a very large number of possible messages at the source, then this potential choice is what Shannon means by information. Confused? Is it because you have too much or too little information?

Sveiby argues that Shannon was uneasy with the term 'information' and considered changing it to entropy, but decided against this as the concept 'was too difficult to communicate' (Sveiby, 1998)[20]. Sveiby quotes Langefors who suggested that a better term for Shannon's work would be 'signal transmission theory'; but Sveiby is rightly dismissive even of this suggestion since 'Shannon's *information* is not even a signal'. This reiterates Hayles' point about the distinction between the amount of information in a single message and the amount in all potential messages from a single source. Shannon and Weaver clearly have in mind the latter view as distinct from the former in their 1959 paper – quoted in Sveiby.

> *If one is confronted with a very elementary situation where he has to choose one of two alternative messages, then it is arbitrarily said that the information, associated with this situation, is unity. Note that it is misleading (although often convenient) to say that one or the other message conveys unit information. The concept of information applies not to the individual messages (as the concept of meaning would), but rather to the situation as a whole, the unit information indicating that in this situation one has a freedom of choice, in selecting a message, which it is convenient to regard as a standard or unit amount.*

Sveiby concludes, quite correctly, that Shannon's 'information' cannot be transmitted. According to Sveiby the best way of understanding this is characterized by Brillouin, who argued that the amount of information should be regarded 'as a function of the ratio of the number of possible answers before and

---

20 I am not sure if Sveiby grasps the – probably intentional – irony in this statement.

after a communication has taken place' (quoted by Sveiby).

So for the concept of information we have two 'original exemplars' – although the word itself has a far longer history – that emerged simultaneously in the 1940s. Moreover Shannon and Wiener were not only aware of each other's work, they were both participants at the early Macy Conferences on Cybernetics that took place from the 1940s onwards. Hayles underlines the importance of these gatherings in her discussion of 'how we became posthuman'. As far as I know the Macy Conferences are not a familiar part of the IS and computational literature (to be honest this is another way of saying that I had not heard of them until I read Hayles' book); yet many of the key participants will be well known to those with some interest in these areas. Amongst others, they included Norbert Wiener, Claude Shannon, John von Neumann, and Warren McCulloch; respectively key figures in the development of cybernetics, the theory of information, the development of computer architecture (including the analogy of machines with biological systems), and the concept of information processing systems.

This is the story of a moment of transformation in the human sciences, an account of a group of people who met regularly from 1946 to 1953 to explore the possibility of using scientific ideas that had emerged in the war years (cybernetics, information theory, computer theory) as a basis for interdisciplinary alliances. The Macy Conferences on Cybernetics, as they came to be called, included such people as Norbert Wiener, John von Neumann, Margaret Mead, Gregory Bateson, Warren McCulloch, Walter Pitts, Kurt Lewin, F.S.C. Northrop, Molly Harrower, and Lawrence Kubie, who thought and argued together about such topics as insanity, vision, circular causality, language, the brain as a digital machine, and how to make wise decisions. Heims, who met and talked with many of the participants, portrays them not only as thinkers but as human beings. His account examines how the conduct and content of research are shaped by the society in which it occurs and how the spirit of the times, in this case a mixture of post-war confidence and cold war paranoia, affected the thinking of the cybernetics group. He uses the meetings to explore the strong influence elite groups can have in establishing connections and agendas for research and provides a first-hand look at the emergence of paradigms that were to become central to the new fields of artificial intelligence and cognitive science. (Amazon.co.uk *Synopsis* for *The Cybernetics Group* by Stephen J Heims)

Hayles' account of the Macy Conferences demonstrates that although the participants seemed to form an uneasy and eclectic concoction – including 'techies' such as those already mentioned, but also anthropologists such as Gregory Bateson and Margaret Mead – they did develop common themes and interests. Hayles explains this as a dynamic process centering on metaphorical understanding.

> Researchers might not have been able to identify in their own work the mechanism being discussed by a fellow participant, but they could understand it metaphorically and then associate the metaphor with something applicable to their own field. The process appears repeatedly throughout the transcripts. (1999, p51)

Thus where Shannon used the term 'information' in a technical and engineering sense, Bateson 'appropriated the same word to talk about initiation rituals, … interpreted … metaphorically as *a difference that makes a difference*'. Hayles stresses the importance of the compounding of mechanism and metaphor, so that 'concepts that began with narrow definitions spread out into networks of broader significance'. Hayles uses the term *constellations* for these networks of significance. This is a far more constructive view of what might otherwise be seen as a web of contradictions and ambiguities. Whether she intends it or not, the imagery of an arbitrary configuration[21] – i.e. a constellation – is perhaps the best way of looking at the plethora of definitions of 'information' that now abound.

Whatever the metaphor, we are left with a morass of ideas about a key concept of our age – following Bauman this might be termed *liquid terminology*. Roszak (1986) may be correct to note that the term seems to be a passive and neutral one that cloaks the arrival of a technocractic political agenda; but it is certainly a troublesome one once consideration of its specific meaning – or rather meanings – is discussed. Within the realm of informatics, particularly within IS and the generic field of computing, such uncertainty has not been tolerated, and there has been a concerted effort to promote a simple model of information. As Mel Brooks noted in *The 2000 Year-old Man*, sometimes what appears *simple* is in fact *eloquent*; but in the case of what might be termed the IS chemical-engineering model of information, *simple* is in danger of being merely *simplistic*.

The definitions given earlier were seen to encompass, or conflate, both the idea of information as *facts* and as the *communication and/or reception* of facts. Furthermore, several of the definitions drawn from the IS literature offer an additional factor by contrasting *information* with *data*. The examples of Senn, and Davis & Olsen are illustrative of this, and just to press home the point table 2 gives a few others.

---

21 That constellations are arbitrary is best exemplified by Homer Simpson's take on the subject

Pepi: Tell me more! I want to know ALL the constellations!

Homer: Well, that one's Jerry, the cowboy. And that big dipper-looking thing is Alan, ... the cowboy.

Table 2 – Characterizations of *data* and *information*

'information is the meaning that a human expresses by, or extracts from, representations of facts and ideas, by means of the known conventions of the representations used' – Zorkocy & Heap, 2003, p7
'Information is data processed for a purpose' 'data can be processed in several ways – classification, sorting, summarizing, calculating, selecting' – Curtis & Cobham, 2002, p3
Data versus information 'The word data is the plural of datum, though data commonly represents both singular and plural forms. Data are raw facts or observations, typically about physical phenomena or business transactions. For example, a spacecraft launch or the sale of an automobile would generate a lot of data describing those events. More specifically, data are objective measurements of the attributes (the characteristics) of entities (such as people, places, things, events).' '... it is better to view data as raw material resources that are processed into finished information products' – O'Brien, 2003, p13
Information is 'data that have been shaped into a form that is meaningful and useful to human beings' Data – 'Streams of raw facts representing events occurring in organizations or the physical environment before they have been organized and arranged into a form that people can understand and use.' – Laudon & Laudon, 2002, p8
Knowledge – 'a human capacity to request, structure, and use information' Data – 'Facts, numbers, or symbols that can be processed by humans or computers into information' Information – 'Data that have been processed into a form that is useful to the user' – McKeown, 2003, p14 *NB McKeown does acknowledge that one person's data may be another's information – but in that case what is the process of transformation?*
'IS are built to attain several goals. One of the primary goals is to

economically process data into information or knowledge.'

data – 'elementary descriptions of things, events, activities, and transactions

information – 'is data that have been organized so that they have meaning and value to the recipient. The recipient interprets the meaning and draws conclusions and implications'

knowledge – 'data or information that have been organized and processed to convey *understanding, experience, accumulated learning,* and *expertise* as they apply to a current problem or activity.' – Turban et al, 2001, p45

'Simply information is the meaning we give to accumulated facts' – Long & Long, 2001, p24

data – raw, unprocessed facts – examples hours you worked, rate of pay – then processed through a computer 'it is usually called information' – O'Leary & O'Leary, 1999, p7

The imagery is stark and clear. Human beings *process* information in a manner similar to a refinery processing oil. In the latter case the raw material is crude oil, and the refined products are petrol, diesel, and the like. In the former case the raw material is *data*, and the products are varying refinements in the form of information. Presumably just as crude oil is *cracked* into components of varying purity, properties and value; so too data is refined into varying subsets of information. So what counts as *data*? Would we recognize it if we saw some? What is the residue remaining after the information has been extracted from the raw data?[22]

According to some of the examples given above, data could be a string of numbers, hours worked this week, a series of characters, or something produced

---

22 The imagery of mining or extracting is not itself without value; for instance Alexander & Smith (2003) in their manifesto for a cultural sociology refer to Levi-Strauss' dictum that the study of culture should be like the study of geology (p11) – but he then makes it clear that this will involve 'diagnostic and reflexive practices.' So this culture mining is not to be confused with mechanistic ideas about data mining.

during a transaction or a space-craft launch. All or any of these are then 'processed' in some fashion. But note that in some cases it is explicit that the processing is done by humans – '*we* derive information from data'; 'information is the meaning *we* give to accumulated facts'. In some other cases it is not clear whether the processing is done by machine or human – 'information is data processed for a purpose'; 'data [is] ... raw material resources that are processed into finished information products'; information is 'data that have been processed into a form that is useful to the user'. In others it seems that the processing is done by the computer – 'data is raw, unprocessed facts ... then processed through a computer'; 'data can be processed in several ways – classification, sorting, summarizing, calculating, selecting'.

I have no idea when this mechanistic view of humans-as-computers first took hold. It is clearly a continuation of a much older tradition that goes back to stories about The Golem of Prague, Frankenstein, Pinocchio and the like. Humans can be seen as machines, and machines can become human or human-like; and Hayles, Haraway and others argue that we are now becoming *post-human*. Many years ago, a decade before the PC was a commercial reality, I can remember taking an undergraduate course in psychology, where the course text was titled *Human Information Processing* (one of the authors being Donald Norman). Unfortunately I no longer have my copy of the book, but I do recall that many of the images and terminology evoked a sense of the individual as a primitive computer; primitive in both senses of the term – i.e. 'an early version of' and 'an unsophisticated version of'. This is not to detract from Donald Norman's subsequent contributions to the field of Human Computer Interaction [HCI]. On the contrary it attests to the power of the imagery that the computer evokes. What we have, however, is a compelling example of the way in which humans have been described in mechanical or mechanistic terms. Moreover, although this is not something unique to the information age, it is apparent that as Bolter has noted 'computers are a defining technology, which develops links, metaphorical or otherwise, with a culture's science, philosophy or literature; it is always available to serve as a metaphor, example, model or symbol' (quoted in Berman, 1989). (The power and potential of the computer was just about becoming a cultural commonplace in the early 1970s: The idea of the brain as a computer replacing earlier ones such as the brain as a telephone exchange or a series of linked TVs – images that were abundant in the 1950s and 1960s. What they all share, however, is a view of humans as mechanisms.)

Bauman has recently introduced the term *praxeomorphic* contrasting it with being anthropomorphic. Whereas the latter refers to attributing human characteristics to non-human entities (animal, natural, collective and inanimate), the former refers to the ascription of non-human, particularly technical characteristics to human beings – i.e. things related to *praxis*, to what we are able to accomplish using technical means. So philosophical ideas about the nature of human existence are often based on existing technical knowledge and associated concepts. This dates back at least to Descartes and would also include Freud's early ideas which drew on the work of Helmholtz who sought to apply Maxwell's theories of electromagnetism to physiology. In the 20th century human intelligence has been likened to a telegraph network, a telephone switchboard, and a scanning device. In the latter half of the 20th century the predominant trope has been the computer and communications technology in general. So intelligence has been likened to information processing (as exemplified by Norman's book) and the brain seen as a natural computer. Hayles argues that the distinction between humans and machines is in fact disappearing as we become *post-human*. So we attribute human characteristics to ICT, and ICT properties to humans. The website http://www.androidworld.com/ encapsulates this in claiming that

> [T]his site is devoted to androids. An android is an anthropomorphic robot – i.e. a robot that looks like a human. Many android developers call their creations "humanoids" rather than androids. We also have robotics links, robot links, animatronics links, and research links.

So presumably most readers of this can be classified as 'robotoids'.

If there is any rationale for continuing to use the term *data*, then its only sense seems to be along the lines of 'something that is stored in objects' – both inanimate and animate. Thus books, records, accounts, computer systems, disks, CDs, DVDs and the like can be thought of as 'containing data'; but then so too do trees, plants, rocks, animals and people. Human beings do not, however, *extract* information from this raw material. The *chemical engineering* metaphor is false and grossly misleading. As soon as humans turn their attention to any object, we are immediately in the realm of *meaning*. If it/they can be said to exist at all, data is the stuff that human beings are unaware of. (This paradox could be seen as the informatics version of Schrödinger's cat, except that once an observer peers the box of data, it immediately transforms into information.)

People cannot engage directly with anything to do with data. Scanning a book into a computer is a data process; someone trying to read it – and make sense of it – immediately is in the realm of information, because it inevitably involves meaning. But to characterize this as a process of *transformation* is both incorrect and highly misleading. Carbon-based entities – human beings or *robotoids* – are information-oriented; silicon-based ones – *humanoids* – are data-oriented. This should be borne in mind when considering the various arguments put forward by those claiming to have progressed towards *artificial* intelligence [AI] – the stress being best applied to the first word rather than the second. Thus one of the key criteria purported AI technology might have to fulfil for it to be judged 'successful' should be a revised 'Turing test'[23]. Instead of a human having to decide which of two inputs comes from a machine and which from a human; the allegedly *intelligent* device should be able to distinguish both between two identical statements made in different contexts and with different meanings, and

---

23 The Turing test is named after the computer pioneer, Alan Turing, and is a test he specified in order to determine if a computer could demonstrate real intelligence – see for instance en.wikipedia.org/wiki/Turing_test

between a sincere and an insincere person – i.e. which person actually *means* what they say?

Just to clarify the position with regard to data and information, consider the case of DNA. In recent years unsolved crimes have been solved once the existing – and often ancient – evidence has been subjected to the latest DNA decoding technology. Here is what appears to be the paradigm case of *data* being processed into information. Surely the data has literally been extracted and then *processed*? But the actual 'process' is actually somewhat more complicated. First of all, what exactly is the data? If say the DNA is going to be 'extracted' from some dried blood or tissue that has adhered to an item of clothing that has sat in an evidence box for 20 years, then is the data the sample itself, or is it contained *in* the sample, or does it somehow appear as a result of the 'process' – i.e. a series of lines or marks on a technically derived image?

And what does the process actually encompass? Is there some material transformation? Does it include everything from the mounting of the sample to the production of the DNA profile, or does it also include the *interpretation* of that result? At what point does the data become information? Or is the distinction so problematic that perhaps we should drop it altogether? As will be shown later, the data-information dichotomy is more than problematic, in many senses it is pernicious, particularly in its propagation of 'classic' metaphors for information and communication – extraction, processing, sending, capturing, and receiving.

Information comes about because animate, sentient, conscious entities – particularly human beings – construct **meaning** and develop ideas in order to exist as social beings and interact with each other. Meaning construction is a key activity in all human processes. A large amount of misunderstanding about the nature of this process of constructing meaning emanates from the metaphorical imagery in which discussions about this reside. This has been discussed elsewhere, particularly by Schön and Reddy; and has been specifically applied in the field of information systems and software engineering (see chapter 3).

Some of the problems in trying to define information are historical: The history of the computer, like many inventions, is one of a transformation from its original form to the one with which we are now familiar. Like some ubiquitous swarm of Drs Jekyll transforming into Messrs Hyde, the computer has come out of the laboratory to challenge and perplex us all. Although some key characteristics of the computer can be traced back to the 19th century and the work of Charles Babbage and Augusta Ada King (*aka* Countess Lovelace, daughter of Byron), its real emergence as a working technology began in the 1930s and 1940s. It was only then that the technology developed in a way that allowed scientists – particularly mathematicians – to trust the electronics to perform calculations at a level of speed and order of magnitude that was beyond human and any other mechanical capability (although pathetically slow in comparison to the speed of current technology). The first use of computers – mainframes – was for mathematical calculations, and later (during WW2) for code-breaking. This highly constrained use of the technology led to the now infamous statement attributed by some to the Head of IBM, and by others to the Head of the UK Atomic Energy Authority, to the effect that computers were wonderful machines, but that there would be no need for more than a dozen or so in the whole world.

The shift to using the *electronic brain* for what were at first seen as far more mundane – clerical – tasks, started even while the early mathematically-focused and code-breaking computers were being developed; but this was a very different use of the technology from that envisaged by its twentieth century progenitors[24]. A team of people working for J. Lyons, a British catering company more noted for tea-cakes and high street restaurants offering an affordable gentility and a reasonable meal, saw that the speed and precision of the technology could be harnessed to large scale bureaucracies. The result was LEO – Lyons Electronic Office (see Ferry, 2003); and it marked the beginning of the

---

24 But not so far away from Babbage's ideas – see Berman's discussion.

era of *data processing*; although the documents outlining the specification for these innovations use the term *information* and not *data*.

The step to using computers for such work had several antecedents, some of which had emerged from use of earlier technologies which themselves provided a basis for the development of computer systems. The most notable example is the use of punched cards – Hollerith cards – for the processing of the US census in 1890. These cards, the ubiquitous *punched cards* that littered computer rooms until the 1990s, had originally been developed for weaving machines – the holes in the cards allowing the threads to be pulled through in manufacturing textiles.

The Hollerith card, like many other aspects of what are now considered to be essential 'computer technology', derived from earlier inventions and technologies that had nothing to do with computers, and have arrived at their 'obvious' and generally unquestioned use and application by a history of changes of direction and serendipity. The other notorious example of this is the QWERTY keyboard, the 'Panda's Thumb of technology' as Gould calls it (1990). Cringely (1992) terms his account of the growth of the high-technology firms in Silicon Valley *Accidental Empires*, and perhaps a history of the computer could equally be termed *Accidental Technology*.

In this hop-scotch historical development – punctuated evolution, or whatever – the emergence and popularity of the term 'data' is just one aspect that is not fully explicable, but is now treated as self-evident, second nature. From the start – whenever this was – it seems to have been (mis)used to be both singular or plural; certainly anyone who used the term *datum* or insisted on matching *data* with the plural form – *the data are* – was seen as pedantic or weird, or both.

Whatever the original rationale, if indeed there was one, the term was soon part of the phrase *data-processing* and necessarily bound up with the use of computer technology in the context of clerical functions in large, bureaucratic practices. The phrase became popular at the same time as the use of the word 'input' as a noun rather than a verb. For mathematical uses of computers, actually entering the 'data' was a relatively trivial task particularly in contrast to the actual computation – calculation using an algorithm or whatever. But for clerical uses, the procedures for which LEO was developed, the opposite was true – the calculation was relatively trivial, but the number of repetitions was huge and the entering of the 'data' was the far more time-consuming and prone to error – on the part of the human operators.

The 'D' word took centre stage, and by the 1960s many large organizations formed data-processing (DP) departments, with DP managers; these far outnumbered those with Computing Departments and Computer Managers. In the US one of the new publications of the 1960s was *The EDP Analyzer* (EDP standing for Electronic Data Processing).

In the US there has been a steady stream of renaming and merging in industry bodies centred on IS-related careers and roles. For example in 1949 The National Machine Accountants Association (NMAA) was established, 10 years later it changed its name to The Data Processing Management Association (DPMA), reflecting its expanded membership beyond finance and accounting professionals. In 1978 The Institute of Data Processing Management (IDPM) was formed from the merger of the DPMA and the Institute of Data Processing (IDP). The IDPM sought to combine 'the managerial orientation of the DPMA, the educational and professional orientation of the IDP and the emphasis on practical data processing in a business and administrative context which characterised both earlier bodies.' In 1997 it was again renamed as the Association of Information Technology Professionals (AITP).[25]

If the renamings seem somewhat overdue, at least they were moving in the right direction. In contrast in the UK there now exists *The Worshipful Company of IT*, established in 1992 – giving new meaning to the term anachronism. Thus this Livery Company has its 'armorial bearing or coat of arms – designed to proclaim a company's identity and objectives'.

---

25 The records for DPMA 1950-1993 were later presented to the Charles Babbage Institute.

The bearings of the Worshipful Company of Information Technologists are symbolic of its work and objectives.

- Vert (or green) is associated with video display.

- Azure (or blue) suggests electricity, the power which enables IT to work.

- Or (or gold) is one of the best conductors of electricity.

- The book and keys symbolise knowledge and access to knowledge, the main aims of IT.

- The mullets or stars scattered on the shield denote electrical force, without which IT could not work.

- The stars also represent stored energy, which can be released and radiates to spread the light of knowledge everywhere.

- The crest features Mercury, the swift messenger god of classical legend, who embodies communication.

- The griffin (half lion, half eagle) and Pegasus (the winged horse) indicate energy, speed, intelligence and reliability.

The Company's motto, *Cito*, meaning swiftly, suggests the way in which technology is applied by the Company's members. It also incorporates the initials of the Company of Information Technologists. (See their website at http://www.wcit.org.uk/)

By the 1970s the term *information* began to appear in place of data. Thus organizations appointed Information Managers, in many cases replacing or renaming DP managers. The Society for Information Management (SIM) was established in 1968. MIS Quarterly appeared in the late 1970s. The information technology was seen as a key component of Management Information Systems. Researchers began to publish findings that supported models of maturity, focusing on growth and change in the use of the technology from basic, mindless automation to more considered and strategic uses.

The term itself quickly became the identifying tag for an emerging field of studies and practices. The growing use of computers linked together with other computers, and peripheral devices such as terminals, printers and the like led to the concept of an *information system*, encompassing far more than a single computer, software and peripherals. As far as I know no-one has seriously suggested using the term *data system*, and it might be better all round if the word 'data' was dropped altogether. Certainly any sustained argument along the lines of the information-is-processed-data argument seems conceptually flawed, futile and potentially harmful. If there are grounds for retaining the word then it would be best applied to data-*management*. We all practise this, particularly now in the age of electronic storage and the internet. I have countless megabytes of storage taken up with items downloaded or saved, but which I have never actually read; similarly I have books and articles on my shelf which I have never opened or studied. If we reserve the word 'data' for all the things of which we are not aware, then this usage seems salutary or harmless – although we might need to distinguish between a) those things of which we are not aware because we have not investigated them, b) those which we are unable to investigate and c) those no-one can investigate; but that is a topic for another context. What is important is the stress on meaning that information encompasses and demands, and this leads on to the topic of communication which is the focus of chapter 3.

CHAPTER 3

ONLY COMMUNICATE

Having discussed information, it is now clear that the term cannot be understood in the context of computer technology without an understanding of what is involved in *communication*: Hence, perhaps, the gradual replacement of the acronym IT with ICT?

Just as the all-too-generally accepted data-into-information model, or metaphor, has to be challenged and jettisoned, so too must the all-too-readily accepted view of communication. To paraphrase what will be developed at greater length in what follows, the key contention here is that communication is a primary, and primarily, social construct, often misunderstood and assumed to be a secondary process which is virtually effort free for the receiver. This misunderstanding has its roots in the metaphorical language used to discuss communication, which in turn has ramifications for our understanding of communications technology. This misunderstanding can only be remedied by closely examining the base metaphor, and offering ways in which it can be resisted, contested and supplanted by alternative metaphors.

Communication as *Making Common*

In his book *Keywords: a vocabulary of culture and society* (1976), Raymond Williams pointed out that the term communication itself originally appeared in the English language in the 15th century as a 'noun of action' derived from the Latin *communicare* from the root *communis* – 'make common to many, impart'. Communication then initially meant the action of imparting[26]. In the 17th

---

26 A thesaurus gives the following alternatives to impart – one set under the heading 'tell' offers – convey, disclose, transmit, divulge, reveal, relate; and also words associated with 'grant' – bestow, confer, cede, relinquish, give. Communicate – gives a group of words associated with 'transmit' and another group associated with 'make known'.

century this use was extended to include the *means* as well as the action of communication – hence *lines of communication*, and the sense in which canals and railways were classified as *communications*. This dual meaning of the action as well as the means parallels the dual meaning of information as both facts, and as the communication and/or reception of facts. In the 20th century this meaning extended to the idea of the press, radio, TV and so on as the communications *media*: So that we now speak about *the media*. Furthermore there is now the distinction between the communications industry, referring to the transfer of information and maintaining social contact, and the transport industry relating to the physical carriage of people and goods. More pertinently for present purposes Williams noted that –

> In controversy about communication systems and communication theory it is often useful to recall the *unresolved* (my stress) range of the original noun of action, represented at its extremes by *transmit*, a one-way process, and *share* ... a common or mutual process. (1976, p63)

What we would now term the 'social construction' perspective is firmly located in the region where communication is seen as a shared process. Whereas the 'transmission' orientation, at the other extreme, lies at the heart of engineering models, mostly derived from Shannon's work. The problem has been that this engineering metaphor – specifically excluding *meaning* – has been used as a basis for models of communication centred on sharing. This has led to people experiencing and approaching communications technology as a technology inherently linked to transmission rather than sharing. Communication has not been seen in a sufficiently widespread sense as a shared practice and a collaborative accomplishment, but rather as one in which there is transmission from an active source to reception by a passive destination; and this is largely how it is has been managed and experienced.

Until relatively recently communications technology was indeed predominantly associated with transmission – or broadcasting: Regardless of the nature of the technology itself, the ability to use technology to communicate required significant resources. Publishing papers and journals, broadcasting TV and radio programmes, making films could only be undertaken as part of a centralized industrial-scale endeavour, with either private or state-controlled resources – or a combination of the two. To some extent this situation is meant to have changed as the technology has developed, so that the centralized and predominantly broadcast structures have been supplemented – and possibly supplanted – by those with an increasingly participatory aspect. The internet has been hailed as opening up communication technology, and therefore communication capabilities, to a far wider range of people: And even the broadcast media herald the era of 'fully interactive systems' and access 'on-demand'.

Understanding Communication – *Communications Technology*

To what extent does this technological development impact upon the act of communication itself? On a wider scale it is usually asserted that the development of ICT has led, or is leading to a new social formation; the information society. This is often anticipated or welcomed in affirmative terms, and authors such as Drucker (2003), Bell (1976), and Masuda (1982) proclaim post-capitalism, post-industrialism or whatever in optimistic or even utopian terms. Others such as Roszak (1986), and, more recently, Webster (2004) question whether such radical transformation is as real or as welcome. Castells falls somewhere in between with his argument that 'all societies are affected by capitalism and *informationalism*, and many societies (all major societies) are already informational'. He explains the distinction between 'information society' and 'informational society' as follows –

> information, in its broadest sense, e.g. as communication of
> knowledge, has been critical in all societies … In contrast, the term
> informational indicates the attribute of a specific form of social

organization in which information generation, processing, and transmission become fundamental sources of productivity and power, because of new technological conditions emerging in this historical period. (1996, p21)

Thus he sees the technological changes as significant and influential, but does not suggest that predominant social forms – i.e. capitalism – have been surpassed. On the contrary he defines *informationalism* as a form of capitalism. What Castells and the others do share, however, is the view that technical development has resulted in a qualitatively different context from what came before. We might now term this *globalization*, again a term that is widely used and the subject of a range of definitions (see particularly Bauman, 1998; also Beck, 1999; Hirst & Thompson, 1999; Held & McGrew, 2003). Whatever we choose to call this, it is now readily conceived that information has become a critical source of productivity and power – succinctly characterized by Castells as 'the action of knowledge upon knowledge itself as the main source of productivity'[27] (1996, p17). More contentiously Castells argues that whereas 'industrialism is oriented toward economic growth, that is maximizing output; informationalism is oriented towards technological development, that is toward the accumulation of knowledge and towards higher levels of complexity in information processing'.

Some of the more extreme – but well-cited and well-marketed – portrayals of 'the information society' have a tendency to encourage the view that this new source of wealth – information, knowledge or whatever – is available instantaneously and universally: On tap through ubiquitous and accessible communications technology. This encourages the belief that problems of scarcity, poverty and disease can be overcome or are disappearing. This places the concept

---

27 NB Castells seems oblivious to his elision of knowledge and information – the distinction is important as will be briefly discussed later in this chapter – a more detailed account can be found in Bryant, 2006.

of 'the information society' alongside cold-fusion and perpetual motion – a something-for-nothing illusion. As J. K. Galbraith has noted, '[W]hen you hear it being said that we've entered a new era of permanent prosperity … you should take cover' (Galbraith, 1999). Castells avoids and dispels this misconception with his analysis of informationalism firmly rooted in historical analyses of capitalism. A similar effort is required with regard to communication.

In his book *Being Digital*, Negroponte (1995) was keen to get his readers to overcome many of the misconceptions that prevent people fully grasping the true nature and potential of advances in communications and information technology. In his discussion of bandwidth he makes the following observation –

> …people … think of bandwidth like plumbing. Thinking of bits like atoms leads to big pipes and little pipes, faucets and hydrants. … The analogy is constructive but misleading. Water flows or doesn't flow. … Bits are different. A ski lift may be a better analogy. The lift is moving at a constant speed, while more or fewer people get on and off. … if I drop a packet of 10 bits every second into a fast moving pipe, my effective bandwidth is 10bps, not the speed of the pipe. (1995, p35)

This is a useful image to start from, since it challenges any utopian, friction-less, something-for-nothing view of the information society. (It also adds something to Castells' image of *the space of flows*, which might seem to commit the same something-for-nothing fallacy.) Information is not simply available at the flick of a switch, and communication is far more than the 'flow' of bits, data or whatever through 'tubes' or channels. Effort is required both to contribute to the information system, and to *extract* information from that system.

One inadvertent benefit of the 'plumbing' analogy – whatever its technical misconceptions – is its evocation of concepts such as the importance of access to clean water; something that many of us take for granted, but which is by no means universally available and which requires input of resources, effort and ingenuity.

This is a useful and sharp corrective equally applicable to those who imply that the information age is ubiquitous, ignoring the awkward facts of the *digital divide*. Consciousness about the resources and effort required to supply clean water, and remove used water, may contribute to our understanding of similar levels of requirements in the supply of information.

Communication & Information

What do we mean by communication? The oldest meaning of the word, in English, can be summarized as the passing of ideas, information and attitudes from person to person. ... I mean by *communications* the institutions and forms in which ideas, information and attitudes are transmitted and received. I mean by *communication* the process of transmission and reception. (Williams, 1976, p19, stress added)

Here Raymond Williams offers what appears initially to be a fairly straightforward characterization of communication, albeit one indifferent to technology; and also one which distinguishes the singular from the plural form – communications; the latter centring on the 'institutions and forms'. His definition of communication appears similar to that offered by Shannon, although Williams certainly does not exclude the concept of meaning from his perspective; neither must it be thought that his use of the phrase 'the process of transmission and reception' refers to the technical, engineering ideas of Shannon and his colleagues. Any confusion between Williams' work and Shannon's derives from their common use of standard metaphorical language to describe communication. Communication is something that flows from transmitter to receiver, through some medium or channel – again we have the plumbing metaphor.

It might be argued that this is *just* a metaphor – a simple figure of speech or trope – not anything with actual and significant implications; but this would be to mistake the nature of metaphor and its relationship to cognition. It certainly is a metaphor, but use of the word 'just' demeans the role and importance of metaphor in our cognitive processes. Metaphor must not be thought of as a restricted linguistic device, employed purely for literary and dramatic effect. This is severely to underestimate the role that metaphor plays in our lives. Fowler's Modern English Usage (1965 edition) notes that 'our vocabulary is largely built on metaphors; we use them, though perhaps not consciously, whenever we speak or write' (p359). This attests to the ubiquitous nature of metaphors, but does not clarify and underline their role in our thought processes. For the editor of Fowler in the 1960s metaphors were essentially passive. More recently, however, this view has been challenged, and it is now recognized that metaphors play an *active* role in thought and cognition. In particular, metaphors are seen as a crucial aspect in the spread and understanding of new ideas and concepts. (Hayles in her discussion of the Macy Conferences notes the critical role of metaphor in the inter-disciplinary dialogues between participants – see chapter 2.)

How do metaphors operate?[28] Any metaphor has two distinct subjects; a 'primary' and a 'secondary'. For example with the term *communications engineering*, the primary subject is *communications*, the secondary is *engineering*. Black stresses that 'the secondary subject is to be regarded as a system rather than an individual thing' (1993, p27). In other words, the term *engineering* is not used in isolation; but evokes a whole range of concepts and terms involved in the engineering frame of reference. The metaphorical utterance then works by 'projecting upon the primary subject a set of associated implications ... that are predicable of the secondary subject'.

Black uses the example of 'society is a sea'[29]; we could use Williams' image of society as 'a form of communication, through which experience is

---

28 This overview of metaphor is based largely on Max Black's essay in Ortony, 1993. Many of the other ideas introduced later derive from other contributors to the collection edited by Ortony.

29 Bauman points out that the word society is itself a metaphor – see Bauman, 2002, pp 41-48.

described, shared, modified, and preserved'. According to Black, the metaphor then operates in the following manner;

- 'the presence of the primary subject incites the hearer to select some of the secondary subject's properties; and that
- invites him (sic!) to construct a parallel implication-complex that can fit the primary subject; and
- reciprocally induces parallel changes in the secondary subject' (1993, p28)

Note that this view of metaphor depends on *selection* by the hearer/reader of aspects of the secondary subject; and that this also leads to changes in the hearer's/reader's conception of the secondary subject. In the case of Williams' metaphor we select aspects of our understanding of society, and fit them to a view of communication. Moreover we also reinterpret 'communication' and apply this to 'society'. Attempting to understand 'communication as a social process' alters our view of both the models and processes of communication, and our understanding of the social. Similarly with *communications engineering* – but note that according to Black's model (metaphor) of the metaphorical processes, it could be inferred that different listeners will select in different ways. Thus someone steeped in Shannon's ideas might select different engineering-type concepts from one who had only a vague idea of engineering but no familiarity with Shannon's work.

Similarly the phrase *information technology* might now seem commonplace, which it is; and unproblematic, which it is not. The metaphor to some is now simply a euphemism for 'computers and other devices'; but the association of information with technology is by no means obvious, particularly as IT is now so heavily slanted towards *communication* more than *information*.

For Black 'every metaphor is the tip of a submerged model' (Note the metaphor!). But how the metaphor actually operates, or is understood is not fully determined by the metaphorical statement itself. Thus the 'society as a form of communication' metaphor might take the form of seeing society *actually* as communication; as *like* a form of communication; or as bearing *some similarity to* a model of communication. The differences may be revealed in various ways in which the metaphor is used or applied; and may have cognitive ramifications. Similarly those who understand communication as a process of transmitting, will view things differently from those who see it as a process of sharing. There are potentially extensive cognitive implications to these – largely unconscious and unwitting – choices. This is not to imply that one or other model is incorrect; but it is crucial to start to uncover the implications and cognitive ramifications of such imagery.[30]

Bauman's writings draw on many metaphors with profound and extensive material and cognitive implications; the most notable in his recent work include the concept of the 'gardening state' and the entire gamut of ideas around his use of the extended metaphor of liquidity and flow – see chapter 5.

Whether or not all cognition has to employ metaphor – Fowler implies this, Lakoff and Johnson (1981) provide an explicitly strong and detailed argument in favour – it certainly seems to be the case that metaphors are indispensable in contexts of novelty and innovation. How else can people grasp the new, other than in terms of the old? Black maintains that 'strong metaphors' act as indispensable bases for generating genuine insights about reality.

> ... I still wish to contend that some metaphors enable us to
> see aspects of reality that the metaphor's production helps to
> constitute (1993, p38)

In other words metaphors do not 'get in the way of actually seeing things', they create and establish the ways in which we gain access to understanding and cognition. Metaphors serve in a powerful, creative fashion; producing genuine

---

30 Note the resonance between the idea of selecting from the secondary subject, and Shannon's idea of selection from a set of possible messages. This requires further exploration, but is beyond the scope of the current discussion.

insight; but on the other hand they also can and do constrain our ideas. This is not simply to suggest that metaphors are merely some form of linguistic baggage that illuminates or obscures reality; they are actually indispensable in *constituting* that reality. In so doing they may help enlighten us in some ways, but simultaneously conceal other key aspects. Hence the need for prevailing and governing metaphors – almost by definition those used without the realization that they are metaphors – to be exposed and challenged, and possibly replaced by others. (This is why paradigm shifts are often initiated by 'outsiders' immune to the taken-for-granted ideas by those in-the-know.) This is the case for the metaphors of communication where the predominant ones preclude or at least obscure some of the key issues.

The creative and challenging aspects of metaphor are discussed by Donald Schön (1993) who views metaphors as generative; explicitly taking issue with the idea that a metaphor is a 'kind of anomaly of language, one which must be dispelled in order to clear the path for a general theory of reference or meaning' (1993, p137). He proposes that metaphor be viewed as 'central to the task of accounting for our perspectives on the world'; and as such 'metaphor' must be understood both as a product and as a process. Thus metaphorical utterances such as 'software development is an engineering discipline', are symptoms of a process of '*carrying over* of frames or perspectives from one domain of experience to another'.

Schön's 'generative metaphor' leads to two issues: The *hermeneutic* one of interpretation and understanding, including use of evidence and justification for a particular metaphor; the *generativity* one concerning the processes by which certain metaphors come into existence and flourish, what Schön terms their 'anatomy'.[31]

---

31 Schön distinguishes between living and dead metaphors – thus examples of the latter might be 'the foot of the mountain', 'the leg of the table', etc. So it might be thought that all metaphors will eventually become dead ones. I would contend, however, that dead metaphors are never really dead, they are just resting, waiting to be reawakened – e.g. one might revive or draw attention to

More critically for our purposes, Schön wants to direct attention to areas where there are conflicting frames, demanding 'frame restructuring' – i.e. domains where differences are not explicable or reconcilable by recourse to facts or fixes, but which emanate from conflicting frames for the construction of reality, and where the only recourse is to 'restructuring, coordination, reconciliation, or integration of conflicting frames'. This is a process that is similar to the making of generative metaphor.

Schön illustrates his argument with reference to a group of researchers seeking to develop a new paintbrush. This new product used artificial bristles instead of natural ones. The brush failed to give the same smooth finish as its bristle counterpart, leaving a surface that was marked by discontinuous application of the paint. The group had observed that bristles produced 'split ends', whereas synthetic ones did not; so they split the ends of the synthetic brush, but with no marked improvement. Real progress was made, however, when one of the team remarked that 'a paintbrush is a kind of pump' (1993, p140); and that painting really amounts to using the *spaces* between the bristles as channels through which the paint can flow. This directed their attention to a range of new factors, such as the curve formed by the bristles of the non-synthetic brush. What in strict terms might be thought of as a mistake – a paintbrush is a pump – results in the generation of new perspectives, explanations and inventions.

Schön is keen to point out that this process is not simply one of 'mapping' from one domain (pumps) to the other (painting). The initial response is one of 'unarticulated perception', only later can one clarify the relationship by interpreting ostensibly different 'tools' as examples of a single category.

This is what Schön terms the life cycle of a generative metaphor. Initially 'one notices that A and B are similar, without being able to say similar with respect to what'. Only later can the relationships between the two be described in

---

'the foot of the mountains' by talking of 'struggling across the narrow neck of land between the foothills and the headlands'.

a 'restructured perception of both A and B ... an *analogy* between A and B'. Later still 'one may construct a general model for which a redescribed A and a redescribed B can be identified as instances.'

If the paintbrush example seems trivial, Schön's more extensive illustration concerns housing policy; in particular the conflict between those who see the issue of urban housing in terms of 'slum clearance and removal of urban blight' and those who see it in terms of 'natural communities that must be protected or restored'. 'It is precisely because neighborhoods are not literally diseased that one can *see* them *as* diseased. It is because urban communities are not literally natural that one can see them *as* natural.' (1993, p150)

Schön's solution to frame conflict is what he terms 'frame restructuring ... constructing a new problem-setting story, one in which we attempt to integrate conflicting frames by including features and relations drawn from earlier stories, yet without sacrificing internal coherence or the degree of simplicity required for action'.(1993, p152)

Schön demonstrates that frame-restructuring and the making of generative metaphor are closely related. 'In both processes, participants bring to the situation different and conflicting ways of seeing ... there is an impetus to map the descriptions ... but [they] resist mapping ... the participants work at the restructuring of their initial descriptions – regrouping, reordering, and renaming elements and relations ....' (1993, p159)

With regard to communication the need is firstly to introduce some frame conflict, challenging the dominant – and mostly unspecified – metaphor: The conduit metaphor.

Metaphors of Communication – *Conduits & Toolmakers*

Michael Reddy's paper, in the collection edited by Ortony (1993), specifically raises the issue of the dominant metaphor that English speakers use when talking about communication. Reddy terms this *the conduit metaphor* – i.e. one that evokes images of waterways, channels, ducts, pipes, streams etc. Reddy poses the question 'What do speakers of English say when communication fails or goes astray?' (1993, p166) He answers his question with examples commonly found in everyday English; these include

> (1) Try to *get* your *thoughts across* better
>
> (2) None of Mary's *feelings came through to* me with any clarity
>
> (3) You still haven't *given me* any *idea* of what you mean

Given the present audience, however, I offer some additional ones from the context of information systems development: Specifically from a requirements exercise, where the clients' and users' views have not been fully understood by the developers, and where the developers have not made clear the trade-offs and constraints to the clients and users – the domain experts.

- The developers should try to *get their thoughts across* better
- None of the real issues about users' requirements *came across* to me with any clarity
- We have not *given* the domain experts *a clear idea* about the technological constraints

At first sight, all these examples seem unremarkable, perhaps devoid of metaphors. Yet Reddy argues that all of them – and many more of their ilk – involve the idea that information is transferred from one point or person to another. Good communication then appears to resemble friction-free, blockage-free flow – the same fallacy that Negroponte (1995) pointed out. Good reception involves extraction and unwrapping.

Reddy lists over 100 variations on these general themes, divided into seven categories, of which the major four are

> - *Transfer* – 'Implying that human language functions as a conduit enabling the transfer of repertoire members

[RM] from one individual to another' – e.g. *put, get, give, send*

- *Embed within external signals* – 'Implying that, in speaking or writing, humans place their internal repertoire members within the external signals, or else fail to do so in unsuccessful communication' – e.g. *capture, fill, include, overload, force*

- *Signals convey or contain* – 'Implying that signals convey or contain the repertoire members, or else fail to do this in unsuccessful communication' – e.g. *carry, convey, contain, be empty of*

- *Listening or reading as unloading or extracting* – 'Implying that, in listening or reading, humans find repertoire members within the signals and take them into their heads, or else fail to do this in unsuccessful communication' – e.g. *find, uncover, overlook, be buried in, expose*

This resonates with Shannon's model. Where Shannon introduces the idea of a *channel*, Reddy talks of a *conduit*. Shannon's model was developed in the 1940s, and he would certainly have been influenced by this metaphorical schema since it is so central to the English language. In the intervening time as technical means of communication have developed, both qualitatively and quantitatively, far beyond what Shannon could have then envisaged, his model – as metaphor – has greatly influenced people's understanding of communication whether or not this is focused on the technical realm to which Shannon's work most readily applies. The misconceptions that emerge from an incomplete or incorrect use of Shannon's, and Wiener's, ideas of communication have proved key obstacles preventing the development of a proper understanding of communication encompassing transmission and mutual sharing.

Shannon's model comprises a source, a transmitter, a receiver, and a destination. The source provides a message that the transmitter sends as a signal, and which is received as the received signal by the receiver. The destination then gets the message: Source and destination may be 'a person or thing'. The transmitter and receiver are connected via a channel. For an ideal process the message transmitted is the same as that received. Shannon's model specifically incorporates the possibility of *noise* altering the signal. The noise may occur in the channel, or be introduced either by the transmitter or receiver. With telephone lines in the 1940s, noise was often actually heard by source and destination in the form of crackling or bursts of static. Noise will distort or change the message so that the received message is not the same as that sent. Whether or not the discrepancy between the two can be remedied will depend on the signal-to-noise ratio and also the level of *redundancy* in the message. If I send you a series of sentences in English, perhaps the words of a well known speech, you will probably be able to reconstruct them even if they are received in an altered or distorted form – for example *Governmend of th5 pe-ple, by t6e 5eople, ffr the peopl6.*

On the other hand if I send you a series of numbers for opening a safe, then it may be almost impossible to reconstruct what was sent initially – e.g. *45 %5 g6 778 870- 43.*

Even if the message consisted entirely of numbers there would be no way of knowing if the message sent was the same as that received – unless of course the safe could be opened, and even then that is no guarantee since the combination received might have been correct, but the message sent may not have been.

Thus Shannon's work was critical in enabling people to develop ways in which the received message could be checked to see if it had been the subject of any distortion or alteration. In some cases remedial action could be taken to reconstitute the initial message, in others all that could be done was to request a retransmission. (What is actually sent; the message or a signal? – see below.)

For Shannon, and other communications engineers, this model provides a basis for a mathematical understanding of the processes necessary to verify that the received signal is identical to the transmitted one – and if not, then to offer ways in which the latter can be altered. Thus Shannon's metaphor has a distinct cognitive effect and several critical practical ones leading to enhanced technologies and protocols from which we all benefit – for example in the form of digital technologies, CDs, and so on. But the general extension of the metaphor into other realms has cognitive effects which have to be confronted and challenged. This is the core of Reddy's argument with its accompanying aim of revealing the focus and ramifications of the conduit metaphor.

Reddy characterizes what he terms the four categories that constitute the critical features of the conduit metaphor

(1) 'language functions like a conduit, *transferring* thoughts bodily from one person to another; (2) in writing and speaking, people *insert* their thoughts or feelings in the words; (3) words accomplish the transfer *by containing* the thoughts or feelings and conveying them to others; and (4) in listening or reading, people *extract* the thoughts and feelings once again from the words.' (1993, p170)

These characteristics highlight similar issues to those raised by consideration of both Shannon's model of communication and the information-is-extracted-from-raw-data stance. Thus Reddy further points out that one sub-component of this *conduit metaphor* characterizes thoughts and feelings as being 'ejected ... into an external *ideal space*, where they are reified, and take on an independent existence; and from where they may or may not 'find their way back into the heads of living humans'.

Again some examples illustrate these features with regard to a systems development exercise.

- Get those requirements down on paper before we lose them.
- We've been trying to pin down that idea for ages.
- There's more than a head-full of issues here.

Having demonstrated the impact and ramifications of the conduit metaphor, Reddy offers an alternative metaphor to assist in what he terms 'frame restructuring'. 'In order to engage in frame restructuring about human communication, we need first an opposing frame' (1993, p171). Reddy terms his alternative *the toolmakers paradigm.*

This paradigm is best understood through Reddy's own example, which needs to be described at some length. He supposes that there exists a community of people living in a compound shown schematically in Figure 2. Each person has their own sector, and no two sectors are alike. The hub of the wheel contains a mechanism for delivering paper messages from one person to another, and this is crucial in people passing on their ideas about how best to survive in terms of building shelters, developing tools, and so on. People cannot visit each other's sectors, nor can they exchange products. At best they can circulate crude blueprints. Any individual only knows about the existence of others as an inference from the exchange of pieces of paper, plus other supporting deductions. Reddy calls this the 'postulate of radical subjectivity'.

Now suppose that the person living in sector A develops a tool; a rake for clearing away leaves and other debris. She goes to the hub and draws three identical sets of instructions for fashioning this tool, leaving a copy for B, C and D. A's environment has a lot of wood and trees in it, but B's sector is mostly rocky. So B tries to copy the design for A's rake, using a wooden handle and a stone head. Person A did not specify the material for the handle or the head – both were wooden – since there seemed no alternative. B completes the 'rake', but finds it unwieldy and heavy; and wonders at the strength of A. He is also somewhat bemused at the tool itself, but eventually guesses that A uses it to clear away small rocks in her sector. He adapts the tool for his own environment, and eventually decides that a better form of the tool will be one that has two prongs to unearth large rocks. This is far more useful for B's sector. B then sketches out his tool design and makes three copies for the others to study.

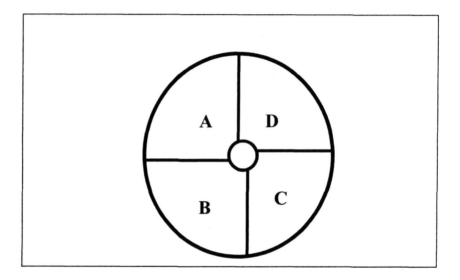

Figure 2 – The Toolmakers' Environment

Persons C and D develop their own tools on the basis of the plans from A and B. Person A makes a tool along the lines suggested by B, but can see no use for it in her own rock-free sector. She also wonders if B has misunderstood her original design, and so produces a more detailed one for circulation. The interchange between A and B goes on for some time, until A comes across two small pebbles in her sector, and she begins to understand that her assumptions about wooden materials and organic debris may not be universally applicable. The result is that A and B raise 'themselves to a new plateau of inference about each other and each other's environments'.

The fundamental difference between the toolmakers paradigm and the conduit metaphor is that for the latter successful communication appears to be gained without effort, whereas for the former human communication 'will almost always go astray unless real energy is expended'.

Moreover the conduit metaphor assumes that communication is perfect unless there is some failure in encoding, decoding, transmission or reception. The norm for the conduit is fault-free, noise-free communication. Conversely the toolmakers approach does not see communication failure or divergent understanding as aberrant, on the contrary it assumes such outcomes are the norm, and that further and continuous efforts are required to sustain communication.

It might appear that Reddy's argument leads to a position that reserves the conduit model for the communications engineers, but tries to constrain its power beyond those confines and instead seek to impose the toolmakers paradigm for more general discussions of communication. But Reddy, after offering an extended demonstration of the complexities of trying to avoid the conduit metaphor, concludes that any such efforts would require creation of a new language. His main objective is to confront the conduit metaphor rather than try to supplant it.

With regard to Shannon's model, Reddy specifically addresses the issue of 'mathematical information theory' (1993, p181). He wonders if 'with both a concept-free algebra of information, and working machines to use as models, the effect of the conduit metaphor should have been avoided. But, in fact, it was not.' On the contrary the conceptual basis of such models 'has been completely obscured by the semantic pathologies of the conduit metaphor.' Thus Reddy allies himself with Shannon's own misgivings about the use of conventional terminology – information, communication – rather than a more restricted and specialized technical terminology – entropy, stochastic processes, signals and noise.

This is not to say that Shannon's work is irretrievably undermined in any way – despite talk of 'semantic pathologies'. On the contrary, Reddy offers further elucidation of ways in which the paradox between Wiener's and Shannon's concepts can be resolved; seeking to clarify Shannon's ideas in terms of the toolmakers paradigm.

> The framework of mathematical information theory has much in common with the toolmakers paradigm. Information is defined as the ability to make *nonrandom selections* from some set of alternatives. Communication, which is the *transfer of this ability from one place to another*, is envisioned as occurring in the following manner. The set of alternatives and a **code** relating these alternatives to physical signals are established, and a copy of each is placed at both the sending and receiving ends of the system. (1993, p181, stress in *italics* added)

In order for any communication to occur, all parties to the communication must have access to both the *code* and the *set of alternatives*. Reddy calls this an 'a priori shared context'; what might be thought of as a shared set of values and understandings. In the example of the toolmakers, this is a very limited and simple set of assumptions regarding interchange via pieces of paper at the hub of the wheel. One could go even further back and argue that even this set of shared assumptions has been learned and so requires some effort and some still more fundamental set of assumptions – there is no way of avoiding this conceptual infinite regress, but it must be stressed that this would not invalidate Reddy's argument. The issue of infinite regress can in part be evaded by treating these assumptions as an independent variable along the lines proposed by Alexander and Smith (2003) in their outline for a cultural sociology where they

> … subscribe to the idea that every action, no matter how instrumental, reflexive, or coerced vis-à-vis its external environments is embedded to some extent in a horizon of affect and meaning. This internal environment … [is] an ideal source that partially enables and partially constrains action (2003, p11)

This concept of communication applies not only to linguistic communication, but also to non-linguistic and non-verbal forms. Aspects such as gestures, tone of voice, body-language etc., can all be considered to be drawn from a repertoire – selected and somehow relayed as signals. Indeed the balance of activity and effort may well lie far more markedly with the 'receiver' – as opposed to the 'sender' – than it does for linguistic communication. In some cases the 'shared context' may not be as mutual as the participants assume – gestures being notoriously context-dependent and culture-specific; similarly such tropes as irony and sarcasm when conveyed by extra-linguistic facets such as facial expression or cadence.

The postulate of a shared context – whatever its origins and however it is developed and sustained – is inherently associated with cultural values and beliefs. The key point, however, is that communication does not amount to exchanging a message drawn from this set of alternatives. In this model communication is initiated by someone selecting a sequence of alternatives – a message. This is then converted into 'some form of energy patterns which can travel quickly and retain their shape while they do travel' (Reddy, 1993, p181) – a series of signals.

It is critical to understand that it is only the signals that are mobile. The signals are transmitted, received and decoded. Moreover, if the process works correctly, or adequately, the decoding from signal to message results in an identical copy to the signal that was sent – itself coded from the message at the source. This aligns with Shannon's view of information as proportional to entropy, since his concept of information is centred on the set of alternatives and not around the transmitted signals. For instance, if I know that the set of possible alternatives consists of numbers between 9 and 99, if I receive a 1 then I must expect one and only one more number. If the set is extended to 100 then I cannot make this assumption. Here the idea of information is that of 'the power to make selections'.

Expressed in this fashion, Shannon's ideas are considerably clarified, and their potential application and extension to communication in a wider sense can be glimpsed. What makes such efforts complicated, however, are the ambiguities introduced by Shannon and his colleagues in their various publications. The key one relates to the idea of *message*, which Shannon and Weaver (1959) used ambiguously and ultimately in a highly misleading fashion. In their original model, they were at pains to stress that the 'received signals' may not necessarily be the same as the 'transmitted signals', since there may be distortion or noise. Yet their model used the term 'message' at both the transmitting end and the receiving one. Even in their own terms the latter should have been labelled as 'reconstructed message' or something similar. (In fact Shannon's 1948 paper does talk of 'reconstructing' the message, but the diagram only uses 'message' at the receiving end.) Yet Reddy points out that even the word *message* is in fact crucially ambiguous; it might be taken to mean a set of signals (M_1), but it might also be understood as the repertoire of members involved with the communication (M_2). Reddy offers examples of each

> M_1 – I got your message yesterday, but haven't read it yet
> M_2 – Okay, John, I get the message; let's leave him alone
> (1993, p183)

The distinction is trivial in the context of the conduit metaphor, since in this context M_1 *contains* M_2. But in the context of Shannon and Weaver's work, and the toolmakers paradigm, the distinction is crucial. M_1 is the only thing that can be transmitted, M_2 cannot be sent. Reddy cites several examples from Weaver's writing in order to show that Shannon appears to have had a firmer grasp of the concepts and been less influenced by conduit thinking than his colleague. Thus Shannon gives a far more appropriate description of the process.

> The *receiver* ordinarily performs the inverse operation of that
> done by the transmitter, reconstructing the message from the signal
> (quoted in Reddy, 1993, p184).

Here the signal does not *contain* anything, it *does* something that leads to an activity: Communication is that activity – perhaps the gerund form, *communicating*, is more apposite and accurate. Communicating can involve some or all of the following – words, gestures (conscious and unconscious), body-language, written texts, pictures, grunts and so on.

Reddy concludes his paper with a revealing story that amplifies the example of the segmented circular compound introduced earlier. He supposes that individuals A, B, C and D slowly begin to develop their interchanges; making slow progress, but always aware of the effort needed to secure adequate communication. Indeed they retain 'a distinct sense of awe and wonder that they could make the system work at all'. But this is all undermined by an evil magician who hypnotizes them so that once they have accomplished some technical feat through arduous communication, they will forget that this happened. Instead they will have the false memory 'that the object had been sent to them directly from the other person'. The result is that the communication system falls into disuse, and the participants assume that any technical construct has been presented ready and working by its originator. This leads to each individual blaming the others both for faults in any artefact that has been collectively developed, and for feeling that they themselves are inadequate.

As far as Reddy is concerned, the wicked wizard is the English language, and the hypnotic spell is the 'bias imparted to our thought processes by the conduit metaphor'. It results in our acting as if communication is something that can be accomplished without effort; or certainly without effort on the part of the receiver – reader, listener or whatever. Far too many of those writing about communication, particularly in the context of informatics, continue to labour under the magician's spell. The chemical-engineering metaphor discussed in the previous chapter is one example; another is the metaphor of *information technology*. The term itself is inherently troublesome since it is used far too readily to cover anything and everything concerned with informatics. Even within the more rarefied confines of IS there is a constant need to make people understand that the technology, by which we really mean the hardware, is not the primary focus of the subject. There may even be those who try to get people to use the term information system (IS) in preference, but usually this is to no avail.[32] The problem is that the cognitive power of the term *IT* stresses the technology – the hardware – to the detriment of the information part.

An issue of the *Insurance Technology Research Report* (September 1998) noted that 'IT is the bottom of the career wish list'. Amongst men 69% dismissed it as a career choice; amongst women it was even higher at 86%. Respondents were concerned that IT was 'too technical', and associated it as a career with nerds and geeks, 'clever but lacking in social skills'. This was partially explained by the link of IT to science and computers, and the fact that in the media 'scientists and computer experts are portrayed [as] ... brilliant but socially flawed and slightly mad'.

The same article went on to point out that the employers who participated in the survey were most concerned at the lack of business and social skills amongst graduates; and that this was the greatest concern among those recruiting to the IT sector. Some even believed that the best equipped graduates for this sector were those who had not studied IT.[33]

Although there are a whole host of influences and factors at work in this example, the impact of the metaphor that lies behind the idea of information *technology* must be acknowledged to have profound and often detrimental effects. In many cases simply substituting the term 'business information' in place of

---

32 And in any case IS is itself ambiguous as was shown in chapter 1.

33 The term 'technology' is now understood to refer to something tangible – something you can kick! Whereas originally it simply meant something connected with knowledge, and more specifically with practice and method. So technology might itself be seen as operating on a metaphorical level; with the original term having been a link between 'know how' and some artefact or invention that demonstrated or embodied that know-how. The advent of IT has now displaced the original meaning completely, so that technology now refers to the electronic components. (See chapter 4 and the discussion on Ellul, whose idea of technology is considerably more powerful and far-reaching.)

'information technology' has had an immediate impact in terms of recruitment to undergraduate courses, leading to a more varied and gender-balanced intake.

The distinction between the conduit metaphor and the toolmakers paradigm is highly significant for many aspects of professional practice for those involved in ICT and informatics in general. One of the most problematic aspects in the development of an information system is what is termed the requirements phase. Here there needs to detailed and mutually comprehensible communication between technical specialists and the domain experts – i.e. those with experience and knowledge of the context in which the system will operate. (This applies to other technological projects, including general engineering, construction, transport and the like.) In numerous surveys of IS development it is the *requirements* phase that is seen as the most important and the most difficult; and the most problematic. In many cases the term *requirements engineering* is used to describe and define this phase, although Sommerville notes that 'the term *engineering* is used rather loosely' (1996, p64). The common, textbook terminology is replete with references to the engineering metaphor – hence *requirements definition, requirements specification, requirements validation*, and so on. The assumption, often clearly stated, is that the requirements process must be systematic, with some element of management and formality. So perhaps the use of the engineering metaphor provides a useful basis for what is widely agreed to be the most critical and disparate part of systems development.

The terminology in current professional use is heavily slanted towards the conduit metaphor, indicating that development professionals treat the process as one of messages being passed between domain experts, users, and developers. The assumption is that communication between these groups ought to be fairly straightforward and unproblematic; and that if problems occur they can be seen in terms of blockages or breakdowns in the channelling of information. The basic conceptual imagery of the requirements phase is bound up with the conduit metaphor. The information about requirements is passed from 'users' to 'developers'; the requirements exist in disembodied form, and have to be *captured* – requirements capture is a standard term in many ICT project manuals.

The March/April 1998 issue of *IEEE Software* was devoted specifically to *requirements engineering.* (The metaphor evokes the idea of a sentient engineer manipulating a mechanical, non-sentient set of objects of some kind – requirements.) The guest editors' introduction (Berry & Lawrence, 1998) is replete with mention of methods, tools, applications and so on. In contrast the journal editor himself offered a view that stressed that 'the field of requirements (and it no longer matters to me what word you like to append to *requirements* to make it sound more esoteric) has to do with *understanding,* not *documentation*' (Davis, 1998, p6, stress added). Davis explained that this realization had only come about some 20 years after his initial shock at being confronted with a document entitled 'Software Requirements Specification'; a title which at first sight appeared to consist of three nouns that took him a little while to decode. Only now did he understand that the requirements phase is not simply about documenting the external behaviour of a system; such a view is partial and misleading. Indeed he stressed that anyone 'involved in requirements needs human skills, communication skills, understanding skills, feeling skills, listening skills' (Davis, p6 – paraphrasing DeMarco). Thus Davis lends clear support to the argument that it is critical and necessary to move from a monological orientation to a dialogical one (see chapter 1).

This parallels Reddy's toolmakers paradigm, since, in the context of developing a shared understanding of the requirements, both Reddy and Davis draw attention to the difficulties involved in providing a coherent and consistent view of the system context, an objective that is inherently difficult and requires collaborative input and genuine dialogue from all participants.

Resolving the Shannon-Wiener Paradox – Communication is a Social Process

Reddy's critique of Shannon and Weaver's model provides a basis for resolution of the apparent contradiction between their view of information (proportional to entropy), and Wiener's view (inversely proportional to entropy). Shannon and Weaver are really not talking about information as such. Their focus is on the transmission of signals encoded from a message that itself has been selected from a repertoire of possible messages. The term 'information theory', given the more common uses of the term 'information' is highly misleading.

Wiener's concept is far more akin to what we might usually think of as information, connected to aspects such as communication, decision making, meaning and purpose. Here the activities concerned may or may not involve technology, but ultimately there must always be some form of human agency.

In terms of the toolmakers paradigm, the Shannon and Weaver model helps us understand the mechanisms for interchange between the participants; the repertoire of possible messages, the encoding and decoding, the passing of signals. Wiener's view assumes that this all occurs, but that it does so within a context where the participants are involved in a series of interchanges that gradually enlighten or inform them in some way. Where Shannon and Weaver's focus is on the potential performance of the technology for passing signals, Wiener's is centred on the human participants. The contradiction between the two definitions of information disappears once this realization comes to light. Critically this conflation of the technological aspects with the human and social ones is a widespread failing particularly wherever computers and communications technology are involved.

If communication is seen as effortless, then the advances in communications technology simply present technical issues related to access, speed, retrieval and so on. Hence the concept of the information society is used to evoke an image of people sending, receiving and retrieving information far more readily and speedily; whereas what is actually being sent are signals that require effort to encode and decode. Again the conduit metaphor underlies this inadequate conception, since it leads us to assume that communication is effortless. Moreover communication is assumed to be derivative; a secondary aspect of reality consisting simply of passing messages about primary aspects of reality itself – real reality.

Williams, writing in the 1960s was acutely aware of the primacy of communication and the need to stress this, and he pointed out the error of relegating communication to a secondary role. It is erroneous to think that 'there is, first, reality, and then second, communication' (1976, p11). On the contrary we have to understand that 'society is a form of communication, through which experience is described, shared, modified, and preserved'. 'What we call society is not only a network of political and economic arrangements, but also a process of learning and communication.' Williams stressed the key role played by language in communication, and argued that linguistic forms had to change to encompass this view of society as a form of communication.

Reddy takes this further with his introduction of the toolmakers paradigm, and specifically addresses the point at issue – communication.

> We have the greatest, most sophisticated system for mass communication of any society that we know about, yet somehow mass communication becomes more and more synonymous with less communication. Why is this? ... We have the mistaken, conduit-metaphor influenced view that the more signals we can preserve, the more ideas we 'transfer' and 'store'. We neglect the crucial human ability to reconstruct thought patterns on the basis of signals. (1993, p188)

The recent explosion of interest in knowledge management, as opposed to *information* management has partly been the result of too close an identification of information management with information *technology*. Thus many of the key texts on knowledge management refer to the necessity to retain the view of knowledge as a human-centred process, and certainly to refrain from seeing knowledge management as a technical aim or accomplishment. (Something that many of the self-same texts then fail to achieve.)

A glimpse of this can be found in the work of Davenport and Prusak (1997). At the end of their book on knowledge management they note that some organizations are afraid to use the term 'knowledge', and so resort to euphemisms such as 'best practice', 'experience', 'information resource' and so on. They quite rightly point out that this reluctance may well be indicative of an anti-intellectual stance that they term 'know-nothingism'. Using terms related to 'practice' or pragmatics excludes many important aspects of modern processes. They conclude that – 'If you call it something related to information, you'll be dragged back to the corporate information systems morass that really involves data' (1997, p174).

Reddy makes his points within the context of his description of the toolmakers paradigm. In more general terms there seems to be an overwhelming tendency for people to resort to conceptual categories that are inherently concrete and technological; and the conduit metaphor is just one, highly significant and influential example of this. This has severe implications for the area of communication, since it is so clearly affected by technology; but where it is crucial to keep sight of the inherently non-technical and constitutive nature of the process itself. Understanding communication as a social process has always been important; but when the 'information society' appears to offer so many opportunities and possibilities as a result of the undisputed technological advances, the human and social nature of the process can easily be obscured. Communication is a social construct and a social accomplishment demanding sustained effort; a process through which we understand and grasp reality. Developments in communications technology significantly extend the ways in which we can accomplish and sustain this, and they may even have some profound effect on the nature of the process itself; but the inherently social character of the accomplishment is indelible.

This discussion has deliberately centred exclusively on linguistic and verbal communication; and even on a fairly formalized subset of this. Communication in total certainly encompasses more than linguistic and verbal forms, although the aspects of communication supported by ICT have until recently been largely restricted to these aspects. But the technology is now evolving beyond these restrictions, both as a result of technological advances and changes in people's use and orientation towards the technology. Rheingold (2003) likens the phenomenon of texting and other more complex forms of mobile communications as the true emergence of a new form of social interaction, which he terms *smartmobs*. He contends that the internet, currently based around fixed or bulky devices is in a state equivalent to the early days of telegraphic communication. This latter technology only became a widespread and significant social phenomenon when telephones were developed which allowed virtually everyone to use the 'network', without having to be reliant upon specialists, specialized contrivances and limited locations. Thus the internet is only now emerging from this equivalent phase with the advent of mobile communications based largely on cell-phones. It may be that Rheingold somewhat over-romanticizes and exaggerates the potential and power of the 'texting generation', but his concept of the *smartmob* certainly indicates a step-change in forms and intensities of interaction that go beyond the standard sociological understandings of terms such as 'mob' or 'swarm'.

Whatever the future with regard to the impact of ICT on forms and processes of interaction and communication it is essential to take full cognisance of Reddy's critique of the conduit metaphor. The recent analyses and responses to the devastation of the Asian tsunami indicate the influence of the conduit metaphor. There is an unremitting demand for more technology, particularly in the form of some intricate early-warning communications system; essentially an embodiment of a super-fast conduit. Yet in the reporting of the events the tale of one 10-year old schoolgirl stands out.[34] Tilly Smith was on the beach in Phuket with her family when she noticed that 'the water started to go funny'. She had been taught about tsunamis a few weeks previously in a geography lesson, and so understood what it meant when the sea receded, and boats on the horizon started to bob violently up and down. She told her mother that there was going to be a tsunami. Her parents alerted those around them, and by evacuating the beach and the hotel many people survived who otherwise would probably have perished. Those now advocating expensive and elaborate technology to provide an early warning system need to heed this example. Two aspects are particularly important, and neither is dependent on technology. The first is that people have to know how to interpret the signs of an impending devastation; many others saw what Tilly saw but failed to act appropriately: And second, there must be a relationship of trust and mutual understanding between the person giving the alert and those receiving it. Not everyone would take a 10-year-old's warning seriously. These are prerequisites for effective use of ICT, and they can only develop based on an understanding of the true nature of communication. Having relied so heavily on Reddy's paper, which deserves far wider recognition, the last word is best left with him.

> I am suggesting ... that ... the conduit metaphor is leading us
> down a technological blind alley. That blind alley is mass
> communications systems coupled with mass neglect of the
> internal, human systems responsible for nine-tenths of the
> work in communicating. (1993, p188)

---

34 www.telegraph.co.uk/news/main.jhtml?xml=/news/2005/01/01/ugeog.xml&ssSheet=
/portal/2005/01/01/ixportaltop.html

CHAPTER 4

TECHNOLOGY

Technology is another of those tiresome terms that everyone uses, and everyone knows exactly what it means until asked to define it – like *time* or *goodness* or *beauty*. If pressed, people would probably start to offer definitions that incorporate ideas such as *machinery, application of scientific knowledge, progress, industrialised production, automation,* and so on. Daniel Bell (1976) and Manuel Castells (1996, pp29-30 and footnote), each in their own way landmark writers about technology, use the same definition from Harvey Brooks – technology is 'the use of scientific knowledge to specify ways of doing things in a *reproducible* manner'. (Castells specifically points out that he uses the same source as that quoted by Bell.)

This has the advantages of simplicity and eloquence. Note that this elegant definition says nothing about machinery or artefacts, it centres on three aspects – scientific knowledge, specification and being reproducible.

At this stage I do not wish to engage with the debates about knowledge, scientific knowledge and the like. For present purposes scientific knowledge in Brooks' sense can be understood as *formalised* knowledge or formally stated knowledge, where there has been codification of theoretical concepts with some practical intent or potential, and where some criteria of rigour and accessibility can be demonstrably claimed.

The concept of *specification* is an interesting one. Brooks uses it in the verb form – *to* specify; and the term *specification* is ambiguous since it could be either the verb or noun form. But in this context there is a close relationship between the verb and the noun, since in order to specify a way of doing something in a *reproducible* manner there must be some tangible *specification* – hence the association with rigour and accessibility above. Engineers – the paradigmatic technologists – operate with specifications. A specification is a plan, a model, an abstraction; but it is not the product itself. No experienced engineer would mistake the plan for the actual product, although there has to be a relatively strong relationship between the 'spec' and the built product. (Software developers – software *engineers* – might argue with this, since in some senses a software program is a specification.) A bridge, a road, a refinery, an engine may change in moving from the drawing board to production, but the specification will or should be amended to take these changes into account. This process of moving from an idea to a specification, which can then be refined in a number of ways prior to construction or application, links specification to Brooks' third term *reproducibility*.

When informatics students – including software engineering and computing students – are first taught about specification for complex systems they need to be taught the criteria of a good specification, as well as to understand that the model is not the system. One way of doing this is to use the '7 Cs' approach: i.e. a good specification should be *clear, complete, contractual, consistent, comprehensive, comprehensible, communicable.* Eventually they also have to learn that these criteria are themselves often mutually irreconcilable. For instance a mathematically stated specification can be proved to be 'consistent', but in most cultures (particularly in the UK) this will not enhance its 'comprehensibility' or its 'communicability'. Such paradoxes are useful in demonstrating that the ideal of an exact science or engineering discipline, capable of providing totally rational explanations and specifications is at odds with actual practice and reality.

So although there is a close relationship between specification and reproducibility, this should not imply that the process is simply one of copying or replicating. Brooks' use of the phrase *reproducible manner* seems deliberate, and stresses that there is a key issue with regard to any 'device' being capable of being replicated, and hence not being in any way magical or mysterious. Also this replication may be on a very wide and large scale, and the replication may involve adapting the initial specification to other uses; and hence not be mere mimicry.

Reproducibility may involve mimicry and exact copying, but it will also encompass using – adapting – knowledge in an innovative fashion.

I have deliberately used the word *device – contrivance* would have been an alternative. A device may be a piece of equipment or mechanism designed to serve or achieve a specific purpose or perform some function, but it also encompasses the concepts of something devised or contrived, including a plan, procedure, technique. A further meaning concerns a scheme to deceive, a stratagem or trick – but that is not something I necessarily wish to evoke at this juncture. What is critical, however, is to note that Brooks' definition and the ensuing discussion have deliberately sought to undermine the idea that technology is something that is invariably about machines and machinery. This will be explained in more detail in what follows after a brief consideration of another awkward concept that seems intimately related to technology – technological determinism.

Ever since someone put the word 'and' between 'technology' and 'society' there has been discussion over the relationship between the two. Does society determine the nature of technology, or is it the other way around? Marx famously noted, in his youth, that '[T]he windmill gives you society with the feudal lord: the steam-mill, society with the industrial capitalist'. This need not necessarily be understood as technologically deterministic, but that is certainly its most obvious reading. Castells in the opening sections of his trilogy offers a succinct resolution to the debate – such as it is – as follows

> Of course technology does not determine society. Nor does society script the course of technological change, since many factors, including individual intuitiveness and entrepreneurialism, intervene in the process of scientific discovery, technological innovation, and social applications, so that the final outcome depends on a complex pattern of interaction. Indeed the dilemma of technological determinism is probably a false problem, since technology *is* society,

and society cannot be understood or represented without its technological tools. (1996, p5)

This resonates with the definition of informatics introduced in the earlier chapters; but how does one start to understand this 'complex pattern of interaction'? Is it something that will only start to come into focus many years after the start of the process? An understanding of the 'industrial revolution', even the idea that the widespread use of industry was revolutionary, only developed several decades after the start of the process. Similarly it can be argued that any clear idea of the information age will only come into focus many decades from now – if at all. Although conversely there are those who argue that the fact that we can now speak of the information age is largely because it began not with the emergence of the computer, but far earlier with the advent of public libraries, universal education and the like – i.e. in the 19th century.

Castells' point about only being able to understand society with its technological tools is an appeal both to see technology as social and as autonomous. Alexander and Smith (2003) make a similar case in their advocacy of 'the strong program in cultural theory', where they distinguish between the 'weak program' exemplified by the sociology of culture in distinction to the strong one of cultural sociology. In this sense Castells is doing *technological sociology* without being aware of it, just like Molière's *Le Bourgeois Gentilhomme* talking prose; and informatics must take this concept of technological sociology into account.

Moreover there is further resonance with Alexander and Smith's account related to their methodological justification for their program. In particular they stress that appropriate and adequate attention must be paid to the full inner meaning of culture, and a similar stricture applies in this context to informatics. Many of the technological utopians – and dystopians – develop their arguments from at best only partial insight into the technology or into the sociology; or both. One of the problems with technical advances is that they are almost always difficult to grasp by those not intimately connected with the technology itself. On the other hand, in considering the wider implications, the people usually least capable of appreciating the potential impact of innovation are the technical specialists. To paraphrase Oscar Wilde – *Non-technicians think they understand the technology: That is their misfortune. Few technicians understand society: That is theirs.* These collective misconceptions are everyone's tribulation.

In the past this paradox or tension has only begun to be overcome once the technology has stabilized to some extent, when its range of impacts and possibilities have become more readily and widely apparent: Something which may no longer be possible given the incessant drive to innovate that characterizes these liquid modern times (see the discussion of Ellul below, and also chapter 5). Discussion of the impact of television only really achieved this in the 1970s, with the publication of Raymond Williams' *Television: Technology and Cultural Form* (1974) providing a useful landmark. (On this timescale we might have been due to achieve a similar basis for understanding computers and communications by around 2020, but that would be on the assumption that ICT itself had remained fairly stable since the 1970s or 1980s.)

Williams' work contributes to the present discussion because it stresses that television cannot be seen simply in terms of the tangible technology: And that the technology itself must be located within more complex processes including systems of consumption, entertainment, communication, leisure and so on. To an extent Castells' work can be seen as developing from Williams' position, although Castells does not explicitly reference Williams in this context.

Williams offers a powerful perspective for the understanding of technology in general. He rejects *technological determinism* where research and development are seen as self-generating in an independent sphere, leading to new social conditions. He also rejects the converse view which he terms *symptomatic technology*, which similarly sees technology R&D as independent, but with the results taken up and used by existing social processes.

He provides examples of each position as follows:-

Deterministic 1 – TV was invented as a result of scientific and technical research. Its power as a medium of social communications was then so great that it altered many of our institutions and forms of social relationships

Deterministic 2 – TV was invented as a result of scientific and technical research, and developed as a medium of entertainment and news. It then had unforeseen consequences, not only on the other entertainment and news media ... but on some of the central processes of family, cultural and social life

Symptomatic 1 – TV, discovered as a possibility by scientific and technical research, was selected for investment and promotion as a new and profitable phase of a domestic consumer economy

Symptomatic 2 – TV became available as a result of scientific and technical research, and its character and uses exploited and emphasised elements of a passivity, a cultural and psychological inadequacy, which had always been latent in people (Williams, 1974, pp11-12)

The two positions, although they appear contrary, share the assumption that technology is an isolated facet of existence, outside society and beyond the realm of *intention*. Anticipating Castells' argument about the relationship between society and technology, Williams stresses that technology must be seen as being 'looked for and developed with certain purposes and practices already in mind', these purposes and practices being 'central, not marginal' as the symptomatic view would hold.

Williams focuses on invention and R&D as starting points for technologies, but he is clear that developments beyond the laboratory or drawing board are social processes. Brian Winston (1998) provides further insights into this with his model of the *process* of invention, and his ideas are of some considerable help as not only has he looked at the process in general terms, but also at communications technology in particular.

There is fairly widespread agreement on the key inventions in the period prior to 1800; the wheel, the fixed stirrup, and the printing press would all be part of any list of the most important innovations prior to this date. Once attention is turned to the key inventions of 18th and 19th century things get rather more complicated, but again any list of 'most important inventions' would include the spinning jenny, the power loom, the harnessing of steam power, and later of electrical power, the telephone, and the telegraph. Moving to the late 19th and early 20th century, the list would have to incorporate aircraft, automobiles, radio, TV, cinema/film/camera/photography, and the computer.[35]

Winston, in presenting a fairly similar list goes on to pose the questions – 'Who invented these?' And 'How did they invent them?' Is the popular image of the lone genius – slightly deranged if not bizarrely eccentric – a correct one?

Winston makes the point that inventions are rarely – if ever – completely novel. The Telegraph was first thought of in the 18th century; the telephone was presented in prototype form in 1854, some 20 years before Bell; the idea of photo-emission that underlies TV was demonstrated in 1877, and early forms of what we would recognize as the transistor appeared in Bell Labs in the 1930s. All of these 'early forms' never got beyond some initial stage, and hence it is the later forms that are remembered as the invention. So Winston poses a further question; why are some prototypes abandoned, while others move forward to become recognized inventions? In other words what is the *process* of invention?

Posed in these terms *invention* can be seen to depend on a variety of issues which are directly technical in the narrow sense of the term. Thus questions of economic feasibility, as well as physical and material practicality will impinge on

---

35 This excludes medical and health innovations – e.g. inoculations, antibiotics etc. – but there is no reason why the model does not apply to them; witness the recent fracas concerning the invention of MRI technology, with the Nobel Prize being awarded to Paul Lauterbur and Peter Mansfield, but not to Raymond Damadian who claims to have invented the MRI scanner.

invention, as will contending and competing interests; and all this will take place within a social and political context. Inventions do not occur in a social vacuum, there will be factors which in combination can retard or accelerate the process. A recent example would be the ways in which the aftermath of September 11 provided an enormous boost to inventions concerned with technologies such as facial recognition, ID cards, surveillance and tracking, and security screening. At the time of writing (early 2004) US immigration has recently introduced retinal imaging and other identification technology as standard procedure, something which would have been seen as inherently unworkable before September 2001.

Winston's model of invention is premised on the distinction between *science* or competence, and *technology* or performance. The move from competence to performance and beyond involves a series of *transformations* – which are socially mediated. Winston sees this consisting of four stages. The first stage is that of *ideation*, and involves the initial move from competence to performance, providing ways of demonstrating that the idea has some feasibility, although such demonstrations are still laboratory based. Only with the second stage does the idea begin to develop beyond these confines through what Winston terms '*supervening social necessity*' implying that the forces are pulling from outside the laboratory more than they are pushing from within. This aligns with Williams' ideas.

This second stage is inchoate and chaotic, it may be lengthy, it may involve many different groups working on different aspects in different places for different reasons – hence the issue of who actually invented what and when. Some prototypes fail to clear this hurdle at the first attempt, often for reasons that have nothing to do with the technology itself, for example the first demonstration of telegraph in 1816, led to its rejection by British Navy who saw no reason to replace use of semaphore – after all there were plenty of ratings to put out more flags!

Sometimes the prototype does become accepted, but is seen in terms of the finished product rather than an experimental prototype; and this can then delay further development. Winston points to early photography based on the daguerreotype, and also to early calculators based on Hollerith cards: They *worked* and were effective, and so this made it harder for people to offer better, more efficient or alternative designs. This is an important point; technology once in place can become a major obstacle to further progress.

Other inventions make their way out of the laboratory but not in the ways in which we now view them. Some of these Winston terms 'parallel prototypes', where machines are used but not in way that eventually becomes their main use. Examples here include physicists using machines to detect radio waves but not in the form of radios; similarly the use of cathode ray tubes, but not for anything connected to TV.

In fact as Winston shows with several examples, a large number of devices central to 20th and 21st century living were initially developed and accepted for uses contrary to their current commonly accepted use. These 'partial' inventions were often intended by their inventors for operation in a manner directly at odds with later use. Inventions developed into their later uses often because they did not perform as originally foreseen. Thus the early telephone was initially developed as a device for one-to-many communication, with one person speaking and their words relayed to a crowd via an amplifier. Hence the mayor of one American city was reputed to have said, following a demonstration of the device, 'I can foresee the day when every town in the country will have *one* of these.' On the other hand, early radio devices were seen as one-to-one devices; and still operate in this way to some extent, although now radio is seen as a fundamental technology for broadcasting – i.e. one-to-many.

Winston gives considerable attention to the invention of the telephone. It is now commonly accepted that Alexander Graham Bell was the inventor. Yet Winston points out that there was intense rivalry between several inventors for this claim. Bell filed his patent in February 1876, on the same day as Elisha Gray filed his. Filing a patent does not imply that one has actually developed a working model, and there is a case to be made that the inventions of Gray and others were actually better machines than Bell's. Indeed although Bell was a prolific inventor, he actually spent more time in suing his rivals and staking his own claims than he did in inventing.

A simple 'who invented the telephone' query typed into *google* produces two other claimants within the first five items. Phillipp Reis, a German, built a crude phone in 1861, and actually coined the term *telephone*. But prior to this an Italian, Antonio Meucci developed ways of transmitting voice via wire, and between 1850 and 1862 he is reputed to have developed at least 30 different models of telephone. Unfortunately, unlike Bell, he did not protect his ideas with patents, being too poor pay for such protection. In 1871 he did manage to obtain an official document called a 'Caveat' stating his claim to the invention which he called a *teletrophone*. Meucci had the last word – to date – when in June 2002 the US Congress recognised him as the inventor of the telephone rather than Alexander Graham Bell.

Historians and Italian-Americans won their battle to persuade Washington to recognise a little-known mechanical genius, Antonio Meucci, as a father of modern communications, 113 years after his death.

The vote by the House of Representatives prompted joyous claims in Meucci's homeland that finally Bell had been outed as a perfidious Scot who found fortune and fame by stealing another man's work.

Calling the Italian's career extraordinary and tragic, the resolution said his "teletrofono" demonstrated in New York in 1860, made him the inventor of the telephone in the place of Bell, who had access to Meucci's materials and who took out a patent 16 years later. [36]

---

36 Source – Rory Carroll in Rome – Monday June 17, 2002 – The Guardian; http://www.telephonetribute.com/telephone_inventors.html

Bell, Gray, Meucci, and Reis all faced the problem of moving from the laboratory to the market place – the transition from Winston's 2nd stage to the 3rd one. The move to the market place may be hampered by the 'Law of suppression of radical potential' – i.e. forces that make it difficult for new products and services to be offered. Winston quotes Bernard Shaw to illustrate this issue – 'Every new invention is bought up and suppressed by Breakages Limited. ... But for them we should have unbreakable glass, unbreakable steel, imperishable materials of all sorts.' On the other hand if conditions are favourable, the adoption of a new product may actually be enhanced by the market – there is a 'constant battle between the accelerator and the brake'.

Again the example of the telephone is instructive as the early spread of telephones was severely hampered in Europe by government communications monopolies that had invested heavily in telegraph technology, and who sought to label the new invention as frivolous and unnecessary. In the United States on the other hand the monopoly had no such barriers to overcome and so by 1910 – 30 years after the technology became available – 1 in 11 had a phone, whereas the comparable figure for Europeans was 1 in 150.[37]

Winston argues that assuming the barriers can be surmounted – which may happen slowly or quickly – there is then a move to *technological performance* resulting in production, spin-offs and redundancies. Thus once a technology achieves technological performance other technologies may be displaced or simply disappear; for example as LPs became available 78s disappeared; as the mobile phone developed the car-phone (i.e. one that only worked in the car) became redundant. On the other hand, some technologies bring with them spin-offs, and the massive video-game market can be seen as a spin-off from the

---

Note the wonderful phrase 'historians and Italian-Americans', and the contrast with the 'perfidious Scot'. As things stand the general answer to the query 'Who invented the telephone?' will almost certainly continue to elicit 'Alexander Graham Bell' as the answer. I wonder if the makers of *Who Wants to be Millionaire* have tried posing this question?

37 Source – John Lienhard, at the University of Houston, 'where we're interested in the way inventive minds work' – see his fascinating website http://www.uh.edu/engines/engines.htm

general developments around the personal computer, and VCR technologies.[38] The spin-offs from NASA's space programme are purportedly legion, although whether or not it was worth funding the space-race to get non-stick frying pans and Velcro is a moot point.

One of the key points that emerges from Winston's model is that the development from *ideation* to *technological performance* is a hazardous one marked by serendipity and punctuated by litigation, rather than developing as a result of rational planning and grand strategies. The Rabbis in the Talmud state that 'if you want to amuse God talk about your plans for the future.' So if you really want to give God a laugh talk about your plans for the future of technology.

In 2000 the MIT website reproduced an article from February 1950 on 'Miracles You'll See in the Next 50 Years'. Here was a picture of a future in which there will be cheap food for all, disposable dishes made from bio-degradable plastic, instant medical care and rapid transport – although still with a division between business class and steerage. Interestingly the author, Waldemar Kaempffert, pointed out at the start of his survey that 'the only obstacles to accurate prophecy are the vested interests, which may retard progress for economic reasons, tradition, conservatism, labor-union policies and legislation'. So even this technological optimist recognized the wider issues involved in actualizing the Promethean vision.

The importance of critiques such as those offered by Williams and Winston is that they afford a basis to discuss and analyze technology as social-but-distinctive. Castells' statement that 'technology *is* society' is a useful corrective against determinism, but it should not obscure the distinctive nature of the technical. Williams is correct to stress the intentional nature of technological advance; it is 'looked for and developed with certain purposes and practices already in mind'. But this is still to allow some autonomy to the realm of technical development.

---

38 See for instance http://www.hut.fi/~eye/videogames/intro.html – on the history of video games

However our present situation does appear to be different, with the nature and role of technology being not only quantitatively different, but also qualitatively distinct. Jacques Ellul offers a way of understanding the wider ramifications of this position. Writing in the 1970s in a manner that is curiously and eerily prescient, Ellul discussed what he termed 'the technological system' (Ellul, 1980, French original 1977) rather than simply 'technology'. He defined the system in terms borrowed from Talcott Parsons, singling out five criteria for the system's sustained existence – a network of interrelations; a preference for constituent parts of the system to combine with each other, rather than with non-system components; parts of the system modify each other's behaviour, so encouraging innovation rather than repetition; the system as a totality can enter into relationships with other systems; and existence of feedback structures.

In using the concept of a technological *system*, Ellul distances technology from any simple identification with machines. For instance some technologies have no such connection – e.g. many aspects of sports technology and medical technology. Simultaneously he stressed the consequences for human action and social behaviour and organization; arguing that whenever there is research and application of new means as a criterion of efficiency, one can say that there is technology[39]. This again resonates with Brooks' definition and also with Williams' ideas.

Existing in this systemic capacity, technology is never simply a 'means' or an 'instrument', but always a 'mediation'. Mediation is used here in the dual sense of *passively* forming an adjunct between two elements and *actively* intervening between them. This goes beyond Williams' point about technology being looked for and developed, since Ellul contends that the modern technological system has taken on an ever more active mediation, until it forms a complex and dominating system that 'fragments, simplifies, splinters, divides;

---

39 Ellul used the term *La Technique* in his writings, and this has been translated both as 'technique' (see Ellul, 1964) and as 'technology' (see Ellul, 1980).

everything reduced to manageable objects' (1980, chapter 2). The 'technological environment makes all problems and difficulties technological'. This is what others such as Habermas (1972) have termed *technicism*. If scientism can be defined as 'science's belief in itself', then technicism might be seen similarly as technology's belief in itself as the means and measure of all things. Putnam has defined scientism as people being 'too realistic about physics and too subjectivistic about ethics'[40], so technicism can be defined as being too optimistic about technology and too dismissive of politics and people. Mowshowitz succinctly encapsulates this with his definition of technicism as a stance that 'mixes optimism and the entrepreneurial spirit with engineering tradition' (1981, p148).

For Ellul, systemic technicism is inherently dynamic and revolutionary. Technology has what Ellul terms its 'functional imperative', everything must be up-to-date; and this imperative is enacted through the system providing its own dynamic, 'technology requires its own transformation for itself'. (This resonates with Bauman's metaphor of flow and fluidity.[41]) Castells specifically adopts this idea in his definition of *informationalism*

> information, in its broadest sense, e.g. as communication of knowledge, has been critical in all societies ... In contrast, the term informational indicates the attribute of a specific form of social organization in which information generation, processing, and transmission become fundamental sources of productivity and power, because of new technological conditions emerging in this historical period. (1996, p21)

> In the new informational mode of development the source of productivity lies in the technology of knowledge generation,

---

40 *Reason, Trust and History*, p142.

41 See chapter 5, also Bauman's *Society under Siege*, p144.

information processing and symbol communication. The action of knowledge upon knowledge itself is seen as the main source of productivity. Improvement of the technology of information processing is seen as a source of productivity. Interaction between the knowledge sources of technology and the use of technology to improve knowledge generation and information processing is of main importance. (Castells, 1996)

This dynamic is only truly achievable once the computer exists, since for Ellul the 'computer – allows the technological system to establish itself truly as a system'. The advent of computers allows large subsystems to organize; providing the infrastructure for growth and administration. In particular the technology moves administrative services from parallel to integrated ones; enhancing their effectiveness and their efficiency. Moreover, Ellul explains that the computer does not exist in isolation, but in the form of 'electronic communications systems'. 'The computer is not a gadget to do things better and faster. Computers are the correlation factor in the technological system ... the computer operates in terms of, and for, subsystems that are technological or that it forces to become technological'. Given that this was written in the 1970s, while the PC was still at best at the level of – primitive – competence this is remarkably prescient.

Ellul's critique resonates with Stafford Beer's position – albeit the latter's was a more optimistic stance. Beer made the point that with the advent of the computer

the question which asks how to use the computer in the enterprise, is, in short, the wrong question. A better formulation is to ask how the enterprise should be run given that computers exist. The best version of all is the question asking, *what, given computers, the enterprise now is.* (Beer, 1981, stress in original)

Thus both Ellul and Beer, with contrasting motivations, are ascribing powerful causation to technology but without falling into the trap of determinism. Castells follows a similar path. What they share is the view that technology makes a difference; in particular that ICT makes a difference. Alexander & Smith follow similar lines in their promotion of cultural sociology, stressing that they wish to demonstrate how 'culture interferes with and directs what really happens'. Ellul certainly does not shy away from doing exactly this with regard to computer-based technology, and in so doing sets an important example for informatics.

Although Ellul could not have realized what developments in computer and communications technology would deliver within the next 20 years, his conception of the technological system and the advent of computers is eerily prophetic, and his observations on the impact of 'electronic communications systems' stand the test of time very well. For instance he stressed the key feature of technological development would be the confluence of communications technologies, so that

> data processing, television, telecommunications .. constitute veritable electronic systems of communication ... we should henceforth speak of electronic communications systems. This specific organism (sic!) is now the new relationship of the technological subsystems, and is allowed by the foundation of the technological system as a whole (1980, pp100-101)

Ellul argued that by the 1970s the technological system was well established as a true system, and had become an autonomous factor, dominating the economic structure. Indeed he asserted that 'technology, as a mediator and as the new environment, makes every reality other than itself abstract, remote and devoid of content'. Ellul's idea of 'autonomy' lead him to argue that, by the late 1970s, the technological system was not simply one amongst several systems, but had become the dominant one. This begs a number of questions; not least how do other systems impact upon and relate to the technological one? Is there evidence or counter-evidence for the dominance of the technological system?

Ellul's ideas have a definite potency; and although at times he overstates the case for the autonomy of the technological system, he was careful to distance himself from technological determinism as much as from any concept of technological utopianism. Indeed part of his work is explicitly presented to undermine such arguments.[42] In the 1990s, as the dotcom boom was approaching its zenith, there might have seemed to be a ring of truth to his contention that the technological system has come to dominate the economic one. By the mid-1990s as the dotcoms crashed to their nadir the nature of this 'domination' was cruelly exposed.

Ultimately the target for Ellul's critique is not technological determinism, but *technicism*; a dominant mode of thought, anchored in the technological system. At times Ellul seems to be simply despairing at the inevitable victory of this all-powerful, continually-renewing, relentlessly dynamic system. In his later writings Ellul specifically contrasted technicism with a religious – specifically Christian – orientation, as if he was intent on finding something that could be set up to expose and challenge the new belief system that placed technology at its centre – with all issues, problems and solutions seen in technically efficient terms.

Drawing on the insights provided by Ellul, Winston, and Williams a simple query such as 'When was the computer invented: And by Whom?' becomes the start of a major critical enquiry rather than a search for a name and a date. We could perhaps start with a name – Charles Babbage; and the date might be the date associated with the appearance of his *Difference Engine*. Even if this was a definitive result – and it isn't[43] – we would still have to prompt for further

---

42 The ideas encompassed by Actor-Network Theory – ANT – in the work of Latour (1987) and others provides a different formulation for avoiding determinism.

43 Babbage produced two Difference Engines, the first was conceived around 1821, the second around 1834. Neither actually worked in his lifetime – Difference Engine No. 2 was finally completed in 1991. His later, even more ambitious device, the Analytical Engine bears more resemblance to a computer, but again it was never completed.

114

information in the light of Williams' assertion that inventions are looked for and developed with certain purposes in mind. We would have to ask in *what* sense was the computer 'looked for', and '*what* purposes are in *whose* mind or minds?'

Babbage, for all that his devices were never completed, was clearly looking for a machine that would enhance the control of the factory owner over the processes of production that took place within the confines of the factory itself. Although now primarily associated with the development of the computer, Babbage was also an influential figure in the development of ideas about manufacture and factory organization. His classic text from 1832 *On The Economy of Machinery and Manufacturers* – published between the development of the *Difference* engines and the work on the *Analytical* one – presented an analysis of the logic and objectives underlying the division of labour required for the discipline and mechanization of production. As Berman notes this is still referred to as the 'Babbage Principle'

> the master manufacturer, by dividing the work to be executed into different processes, each requiring different degrees of skill or force, can purchase exactly that precise quantity of both which is necessary for each process; whereas, if the whole work were executed by one workman, that person must possess sufficient skill to perform the most difficult, and sufficient strength to execute the most laborious, of the operations into which the art is divided (Babbage, 1832, pp175-6 – quoted by Berman, 1989, p12)

Babbage took Adam Smith's ideas about the division of labour and further clarified them, having been particularly impressed by the ways in which the French had applied the division of labour in the production of mathematical tables.[44] Whereas Smith's famous description of the manufacture of pins is an example of predominantly horizontal division of labour – i.e. with increasing

---

44 Babbage and Herschel visited France in 1819 to observe these table producing 'factories'.

functional specialization – Babbage was interested in the operation of the vertical division of labour; specifically hierarchical and incorporating a top-down, and command-and-control structure.[45]

So there is a good deal of evidence for the claim that this pioneer in computer technology was drawn to the idea from his interests in factory management, particularly the division of labour and work organization, as well as his interest in producing accurate computational tables; and also that he obtained substantial government funding because this interest was more widely shared and encouraged. Berman has pointed out that Babbage had identified three principles of factory organization before he began work on his various devices. The first of these was *hierarchy*, and the other two were *sequence of control* and *iteration*. Hierarchy is self-explanatory, and relates to the vertical division of labour. Sequence of control refers to linking together a number of activities in a logical and coherent sequence in order to maximize efficiency and reduce wastage – of material and effort; echoing Smith's horizontal division of labour. Iteration in this context refers to the repetition of processes or activities within some larger overall objective. These all are encompassed by Babbage's – and other's – concern with the need to enhance the control, planning and co-ordination of factory-based manufacture.

In an earlier chapter mention was made of Bauman's concept of *praxeomorphism*. Here is another double-edged example linking technology to industrial practice. The technology was shaped in a way that mirrored factory management. In fact the technology did not quite work in the late 19th century, although the structure of computers that did work in the 20th century bore a close resemblance to Babbage's conception specifically offering processing in terms of hierarchy, sequence and iteration.[46] In the meantime, however, Taylorism had

---

45 The distinction between Smith's concept and Babbage's parallels that between markets and hirerarchies.

46 For a fascinating account of what 19th century computer technology might have looked like, had Babbage's machines been made to work, see Gibson & Sterling, *The Difference Engine*.

gained ground; and this inexorably took the shape of manufacturing technology and applied it to humans. When ICT finally did develop as a practical and feasible technology in the latter half of the 20th century it was immediately and obviously applicable to many aspects of the value chain previously resistant to Taylorism; particularly clerical aspects. By the last decades of the century ICT would also pervade the managerial fiefdom and so come ever closer to completing the Taylorist agenda, which was also Babbage's agenda.[47] This is not to argue that the technology was inevitably leading to this outcome; although Ellul, Berman, and Weizenbaum (1984) all argue that the computer was an answer to a series of problems that had long preceded its eventual appearance.

If we follow Winston's ideas then the invention of the computer (and we are talking here of mainframe computers, not PCs) has to be seen as a far more complicated and lengthy process than simply the appearance of Babbage's machines. His *Difference Engines* bear little or no resemblance to anything we might call a computer; his later *Analytical Engine* is perhaps more recognisably a primitive computer, but it never actually worked. The first machines that actually resemble a computer only started to operate in the 1930s. For instance Konrad Zuse's Z1 Computer is recognised as the first programmable machine (1936). By the 1940s there were various contenders, including machines built by Atanasoff and Berry (1942 – ABC Computer), Aiken and Hopper (1944 – Harvard Mark 1), and Eckert and Mauchly (1946 – ENIAC 1). All these machines relied heavily on ideas drawn from Turing, von Neuman and other theoretical luminaries, so calling Babbage the inventor of the computer would be even more bizarre than calling Leonardo Da Vinci the inventor of the aeroplane.

Moreover, the computer of the 1930s and 1940s was a machine for *number-crunching*, predominantly developed for mathematical purposes, and later as part of the war effort for deciphering and decoding. Hence the infamous

---

47 The full history and impact of Taylorism has yet to be written, but it was a central component of the 20th century, and remains so in the 21st. I would argue that the 21st century will be even more the era of Taylorism than the 20th century.

statement – attributed both to the head of IBM and the UK Atomic Energy Commission – to the effect that while computers are a good thing, there will only be the need ten or twelve in the whole world. The idea of using computer technology for repetitive, clerical tasks – *data-processing* – was the 'invention' of a group of people working for Lyons Tea Houses in the UK in the 1940s.

The machine was called LEO – Lyons Electronic Office – and was built after an earlier one had been completed by engineers at Cambridge University. It started operation in the early 1950s, and many of the specific requirements for LEO had a key impact on the development of computer technology for clerical and non-mathematical procedures. There was no point developing a machine that could do vast, complex calculations at super-human speed if it relied upon an army of human clerical assistants to set up and feed in the information. Mathematical use of computers was simple in comparison to the challenges that had to be met in order for clerical procedures to be carried out by machine. Thus LEO had to have reliable and straightforward mechanisms for input and output; something that previously had not been a primary issue. Interestingly many of the websites with time-lines and the like for the development of the computer fail to mention LEO – an unpardonable error.[48]

When it comes to the personal computer the process of invention is even more obviously a mixture of serendipity and litigation. The transistor was developed in the late 1940s, and the integrated circuit (the computer *chip*) in the late 1950s. In the 1970s Intel produced the first micro-processors, and by the end of that decade non-business consumers were being targetted with personal computers. By 1980 IBM entered the fray – most unwillingly – and the PC-era truly started. But as Robert Cringely (1992) has noted, the businesses that emerged in the light of these developments were truly *Accidental Empires*.

---

48 For a readable and accessible account of LEO, set within the context of computer development and operation in general, see Georgina Ferry's excellent book *A Computer Called LEO*.

Personal computers made it possible for businesses to move further and faster than they ever had before, creating untold wealth that we had to spend on *something*, so we all became shoppers. ... And I'm here to tell you three things: 1. It all happened by accident. 2. The people who made it happen were amateurs. 3. And for the most part they still are. (Cringley, 1992, pp4-5)

Many aspects of the computer were reliant on pre-existing technology. For many years input was produced in the form of data cards that were simply updated and extended punched cards – first used by Jacquard in 1801 for automated weaving machines, and later most notably by Hollerith in the US census in 1890. These cards are no longer used, but the primary input device also dates from an earlier technology – the QWERTY key board – what S.J. Gould has described as the 'Panda's Thumb of technology'. Pandas do not actually have thumbs, they have five fingers – all aligned, and so not transposable like a human thumb. But a small bone in their wrist has developed and enlarged so that it serves as a thumb, allowing pandas to pick up and strip off bamboo stalks. Gould quotes Darwin – 'Although an organ may not have been originally formed for some special purpose, if it now serves for this end we are justified in saying that it is specially contrived for it.' (Gould, 1990, p25) And Darwin goes on to state that if a human contrivance was developed in the same way – utilising existing parts – then it might be said that these existing parts 'were specially contrived for that purpose'.

Using Winston's model the typewriter might be seen as a redundant technology or a partial prototype; but using Darwin's imagery the QWERTY keyboard can be seen as 'specially contrived' – noting particularly the connotation of artificiality in Darwin's term. For both Winston and Darwin (via Gould) there is no invention *sui generis*, but there is contrivance; and where there is human contrivance – specifically for Winston but not for Darwin – there will be debates and contention over motivation, primacy and origin: Thus the current debates on

MRI technology, the different origins of computer technology, and even the disputed explanations for the persistence of the QWERTY keyboard (itself a culturally or rather linguistically specific artefact).

Winston's model, together with Williams' idea of technical solutions being 'looked for', also sheds light on the development of the internet and the world wide web. The former emerged from military demands for resilient communications networks; and the latter is now traced back to the writings of Vannevar Bush in the 1940s prior to the pioneering work of Tim Berners-Lee who was seeking a form of records management for his colleagues at CERN.[49]

What Ellul, Williams, Winston and others of their ilk demonstrate is summarized by Ellul as follows –

> each new technological element is merely one more brick in the entire edifice, a cog in the machine, coming just in time to perform a function never before carried out, to fill a space that, we now realize, was a gap. ... The computer has entered a perfectly oriented system... (p110)

Ellul tends to assume that the technology works or is effective, and that the technological system becomes completely dominant; *a prison house of technology*. Williams is far more sceptical, and his approach allows us to explain some of the examples Winston gives of 'rejected, early prototypes'. The intentions are readily understood, the technology did not, however, fulfil the expectations. Artificial intelligence is a prime and expensive example. Reading several of the recent accounts of the development of computers and particularly the changes in the architecture of the PC, Williams' stress on *intention* in R&D explains a good deal. Many aspects of the personal computer came about almost

---

49 see for instance the following websites – http://home.earthlink.net/~dcrehr/ and
http://www.ideafinder.com/history/inventions/story072.htm

by accident, but equally many relied on very specific decisions and intentions. There is a fairly well documented story about the founding of Compaq, a company that was extremely influential in PC developments in the 1980s. The three founders of Compaq, all ex-employees of Texas Instruments, could not decide whether they should 'open a Mexican restaurant, build hard disk drives ... or manufacture a gizmo that would beep on command to help find lost car keys' (Cringely, 1992, p171); and only as an afterthought did they consider manufacturing IBM clones: Needless to say the draft business plan was sketched out on a restaurant place mat. The story of the decision by IBM to choose Microsoft's DOS operating system, rather than CP/M illustrates a even more bizarre case of serendipity. According to Cringely the developer of CP/M – Gary Kildall – opted to go flying rather than meet the IBM team, who instead headed off to meet their second choice, an unknown called Bill Gates.

Despite their differences, Williams' and Ellul's approaches to technology are a considerable advance over those who continue to place far too much emphasis on the tangible aspects of the technology; a sort of *gee-whiz* theory of history which allocates primacy to something, which although initially wondrous and remarkable, just does not seem to provide quite the powerful social impetus that many would have us believe. As was already mentioned, a further strand to this perspective extends beyond the technology itself, and lauds the inventors as heroes. This is then followed by the suggestion that the experts involved with the technology should widen their remit from the technical to the social realm. To the non-specialist a certain range of technical skills appear to produce almost magical effects. The temptation is then to suppose that the skills which produce this authority and control can be applied to society – viewed as mechanism writ large. This position was stated with great clarity by Thorstein Veblen in the 1920s who saw engineers (the paradigm example of professional technocrats) as the natural decision makers for all matters non-technical as well as technical. In contrast, Robert Merton argued that such members of the managerial bureaucracy are imbued with a 'trained *incapacity* for thinking about and dealing with human affairs' (see Bryant, 2000).

The parameters of this dispute are not simply a matter of historical interest since from the 1980s onwards we have simply substituted 'business*man*' for engineer as the 'natural decision maker'. In both cases there is a misplaced faith in rationalism, and a confusion of rhetoric with reality, usually articulated in the form of an all-encompassing plan; sometimes called a business plan, more commonly for engineers, a specification. This might be seen as further proof of Ellul's argument for the predominance of the technological system, exemplified by the ways in which Bill Gates is received by heads of state with at least the status of their equal, if not their superior.

What is needed is not to allow the engineers to run society, but to ensure that social actors come to understand the full ramifications and meanings of technology. Veblen's ideal is sometimes seen as having achieved an actual embodiment in the development of Singapore once Lee Kuan Yew rose to prominence in the 1970s. K.L. Phua (nd) analyzes this in his paper entitled *Veblen's Singapore*, noting that many of the key political personnel have perfect technocractic profiles easily aligning with the 'Singaporean emphasis (some would say *overemphasis*) on meritocracy, efficiency, productivity and competitive, high achieving performance'. While readily accepting that in stark economic terms Singapore has made remarkable progress, Phua also points to the down-side, particularly the authoritarianism and paternalism. Singapore has developed in ways that Veblen never could have imagined, so that it is now 'better labelled as *Max Weber's Singapore* rather than *Thorstein Veblen's Singapore*, i.e. a society which emphasizes (overemphasizes?) instrumental rationality to the point where the *iron cage of rationality* is a real threat' to all. In fact Phua is more equivocal than William Gibson who described Singapore as 'Disneyland with the death-sentence'.

Recent work on globalization in the writings of Bauman, Giddens and others seems to point to the Singapore experience as the precursor of wider social and political changes, rather than a one-off experiment. The development of information and communications technology has not caused this, but is intimately bound up with such phenomena. Weizenbaum echoing the same ideas as Williams, has stated that the 'remaking of the world in the image of the computer started long before there were any electronic computers' (1984, p *ix*). Berman makes a similar point: 'If the growth of capitalism based on hierarchy, controlled sequence and rapid iteration remade the world in the image of the computer, then the seemingly uncontrollable growth of corporate and state bureaucracy was the crisis that was averted by the computer's appearance' (1989, p23).

Weizenbaum, in a response to Daniel Bell, makes the point as follows. Herbert Hoover, US Secretary of Commerce in 1920s, at the dawn of commercial radio broadcasting, and as mass TV became a reality, articulated a euphoric dream when

> these media would exert an enormously beneficial influence on the shaping of American culture. Americans of every class, most particularly children, would, many for the first time, be exposed to the correctly spoken word, to great literature, great drama …
>
> The technological dream was more than realized. … But the cultural dream was cruelly mocked .. magnificent technology … [an] exquisitely refined combination of some of the human species' highest intellectual achievements …. delivering an occasional gem buried in immense avalanches of everything that is most banal or insipid or pathological in our civilization. (1980, pp553/4)

At the start of this chapter I used a definition of technology from Harvey Brooks, and I also stressed that it had been used both by Daniel Bell and Manuel Castells. But Brooks also offers a further definition

Technology refers to the type of relationship established between labour and matter in the production process through the intermediation of a given set of means of production enacted by energy and knowledge

This is a far more complex statement since it specifically introduces concepts of labour, production process, energy and knowledge. This evokes issues about the nature of society, relations of production, and culture and so it is to these that attention will now be turned, advancing the explanation of Haraway's enhanced definition of *informatics* that was introduced in chapter 1.

PART THREE

INFORMATICS AND LIQUID MODERNITY

CHAPTER 5

LIQUID MODERNITY: MILESTONES & MAELSTROMS

The previous chapters have sought to clarify and ground the concepts of *informatics, information, communication,* and *technology.* Haraway's definition has been slightly modified and extended so that informatics is the study of 'technologies of information *and communication* as well as the biological, social, linguistic and cultural changes that initiate, accompany and complicate their development'. Leaving aside the *biological* aspects for the moment; for the social, cultural and linguistic changes we need to be able to grasp the current thinking and analyses that are on offer from various disciplines – specifically in the social sciences and humanities. The predominant and most relevant term used by theorists and politicians and policy makers is *the information society.*

A significant literature has developed portraying the range of different stances on the nature and specificity of existing society, comparing and contrasting different positions across a variety of axes. One of the most recent collections on *The Information Society* (Webster, 2004) notes that the term itself 'certainly is evocative, but it is simultaneously fuzzy and evasive' (p10). Webster warns readers of the edited collection of articles that they should note different writers' use of 'definitional terms used, often tacitly ... Are they, for instance, emphasizing the economic, educational or cultural dimensions when they discuss the Information Society, or is it technology which is given the greatest weight in their accounts?' A similar caveat needs to be raised for all other similar summaries of debates over the many other terms used for contemporary society; but on the other hand there is no avoiding these conceptual morasses if one is to start to understand and account for the (biological), social, linguistic and cultural changes that initiate, accompany and complicate the development of ICTs.

128

One key form of 'evasion and fuzziness' is not specifically mentioned by Webster, but continues to beset many grand sociological pronouncements concerned with the nature of the information society: It concerns the status of the analysis on offer. Is it truly an analysis of the present, a glimpse of the future, an avocation or a warning, or a specification? In many cases it is a mixture of several of these, and one of the most notable exemplars of such confusion and elision can be found in the work of Daniel Bell.

Bell initiated and impelled the most recent trend of proclaiming and (re)naming the social form that either already exists or is coming into existence – or is desired – with his work in the 1970s on *Post-industrial Society* (1976, 1979). Bell can justifiably claim a remarkable degree of foresight in his work on post-industrial society. The essay itself was published before the commercial advent of the PC and many of his ideas have been taken up as common currency by those writing about the information society. Yet despite his prescience, not quite at the same profound level as that of Ellul, one of the most notable aspects of Bell's work is his consistent conflation of reality with specification; the earliest example of this is in his work on *the end of ideology* from the 1950s and 1960s (1961). Here he continually conflated several important but distinct arguments – an analysis of society that claimed to describe a distinct and noteworthy trend – what might be termed *the ending of ideology*; that ideologies ought to wither and expire – *the end to ideology*; a commitment to combat ideologies – *putting an end to ideology*.

Bell used the term of the time – ideology – but his target was clearly and specifically Marxism; although he was adamant that he was not advocating stasis and conservatism; but, on the contrary, wished to encourage the development of utopian ideas – albeit with an eerie premonition of the 1980s and Thatcherism. For Bell, discussion and consideration of utopias was a necessary part of social and political existence, but unlike ideologies – based on (groundless) faith – utopias must have an empirical basis.

> ... a utopia has to specify <u>where</u> one wants to go, <u>how</u> one
> wants to get there, the costs of the enterprise, and some
> realisation of, and justification for the determination of <u>who</u>
> is to pay (1961, p408)

Bell termed this 'an empirical ladder to heaven'. From the 1980s onwards we would call it a business plan; the ultimate effacement of the distinction between 'is' and 'ought' (or 'is and bought'). By the late 1970s Bell had himself moved from an engagement with Marxism and Communism to a consideration of society in which the technological future looked bright and rosy. Like a latter day Lincoln Steffens, Bell almost seemed ready to proclaim that he had 'seen the future and it works!'

Starting in the early 1970s, Bell proclaimed the coming of *post-industrial society,* where problems of scarcity would gradually be overcome, and society would move from a focus on production to a focus on services, quality and knowledge. By the later 1970s, Bell started to use the term *Information Society* instead of post-industrial society – but the two are virtually synonymous in his work. In 1973, in his proclamation of the coming of post-industrial society, Bell asserted that 'the post-industrial society is an information society'.

Here again we have a conflation of social analysis and social forecasting and political programme. Bell is keen to highlight trends in use of technology, decline in manufacturing in favour of services and professions, and apparent political and cultural changes. A careful reading of his work, particularly *The Coming of Post-Industrial Society* highlights this mixture of analysis, prejudgement and optimistic preconception.

> A post-industrial society is based on services. Hence, it is a
> game between persons. What counts is not raw muscle power, or
> energy, but information. The central person is the professional, for
> he is equipped, by his education and training, to provide the kinds of
> skill which increasingly are demanded in the post-industrial society.

If an industrial society is defined by the quantity of goods as marking a standard of living, the post-industrial society is defined by the quality of life as measured by services and amenities – health, education, recreation, and the arts – which are now deemed desirable and possible for everyone. (Bell extract in Webster, 2004, p87)

It is not surprising that Giddens has dubbed Bell 'advanced capitalism's most persuasive salesman'. But he is closely followed and volubly supported by a large sales-support team including Toffler (1973), Naisbitt (1982), Masuda (1982), Drucker (2003) and many others; proffering alternative or complementary catchphrases such as 'Third Wave', 'Megatrends', 'Computopia', 'The Knowledge Society', and so on.

The visions and analyses of Bell et al – the *info-utopians* – stand in sharp contrast to the work of those who have taken specific issue with such roseate reasoning.[50] Moreover such utopianism stands in stark contrast to those who portray the digital future – or present – in far more pessimistic terms, often using literary devices rather than sociological ones. The sinister side of the digital future is currently best evoked by the writings of William Gibson (1995), Phillip K Dick (2000, 2004), and Kurt Vonnegut (1999); these offer a view of the near-future, or distant-present, which directly contradicts Bell's sales patter. To correct Lincoln Steffens' exhortation; they have seen the future and it *doesn't quite work*, nor do most of the people.

J. K. Galbraith has offered a timely and salutary warning, well worth constant reiteration, with regard to those announcing any imminent utopia:

When you hear it being said that we've entered a new era of permanent prosperity with prices of financial instruments reflecting that happy fact, you should take cover. This has been the standard

---

50 Ian Angell's evocatively titled *The New Barbarian Manifesto* (2000) exemplifies the position of those who recognize the dystopian nature of informaion society, but seek to provide some form of reconciliation.

justification of speculative excess for several centuries. Let us not assume that the age of slump, recession, depression is past. (lecture at LSE June 1999)

The elision or conflation of the *is* with the *ought*; the analysis of the actual with the specification or design for the desirable, is not too surprising. After all Bell is arguing for a reality that does not (yet) exist; but perhaps it might in the immediate future, if all the best aspects of identified trends continue and outpace and efface the unwelcome aspects. This resonates with the graffiti dating back at least to the 1960s – 'The meek shall inherit the earth; if that's alright with everyone else'.

Moreover, there is an uneasy duality in the info-utopian argument; defining the desired end both in contrast with what has gone before – or is disappearing – and what is new and emerging. This duality is expressed in the whole host of terms that either point to what we have surpassed – *post*-modern; *post*-capitalist; *post*-industrial; *post*-Fordist; or what we have become or are becoming – information-*society*, informational-*society*, digital-*society*, knowledge-*society*, globalized-*society*, network-*society*. All these avocations and invocations derive from efforts to characterize the social and political; specifying the continuities and discontinuities with what has gone before. There is a near-universal acknowledgement that the discontinuities are closely associated with ICTs, but the nature and extent of the discontinuities and associations are the critical and substantive issues over which the various analyses differ.

Whatever one's misgivings or preferences, the term *information society* is now the common coin. In 1993 The European Union commissioned a report – later termed The Bangemann Report (1994) – on *Europe and the Global Information Society*. 'This Report urges the European Union to put its faith in market mechanisms as the motive power to carry us into the Information Age.'

The Bangemann report with its clear emphasis on 'fostering an entrepreneurial mentality' has led to the creation of an EU 'Directorate General

Information Society' accompanied by the usual panoply of Commissioners and Eu-rocrats. At the time of writing, their website seems mostly concerned with de-regulation and standardization, primarily with regard to mobile telecommunications (July 2005). If Daniel Bell is the ad-man for advanced capitalism, the Bangemann Report is the proto-business plan for the information society. Both are part of a concerted trend to proclaim that the source of universal salvation is to be found in harnessing ICT; only by giving technological entrepreneurialism free rein can this be accomplished. It is telling that the website itself – 'Europe's Information Society Thematic Portal'[51] – lists two items under the heading 'Society & Culture'; they are *eGovernment* and *eInclusion*. This latter relating to 'Participation for all in the Knowledge-based Society' (sic); aimed at ensuring 'that every citizen should have the appropriate skills needed to live and work in a new Information Society for all' – a limited and strangely technocratic characterization of 'inclusion' (and by extension of *exclusion*), an objective clarifying the way in which modern governments are turning themselves into global employment agencies.

A more recent example of these themes can be found with regard to the UN hosted *World Summit on the Information Society* (December 2003), the conclusion to a process initiated in 2001 when the United Nations General Assembly adopted Resolution 56/183 'concerning the organization of a World Summit on the Information Society (WSIS)'. The status and core concerns of this summit were somewhat obscure and unusual. Usually summits are called to bring – selected – governments together to discuss some pressing issue such as climate change, arms control, poverty and the like. So to what extent is the *information society* an issue of this kind? Moreover, the remit of those invited to attend the summit extended beyond the usual sovereign members, to include 'other intergovernmental organizations, including international and regional institutions, non-governmental organizations, civil society and the private sector to contribute

---

51 http://europa.eu.int/information_society/index_en.htm

to, and actively participate in, the intergovernmental preparatory process of the Summit and the Summit itself'.

This combination of all the great and good – governmental, non-governmental [NGOs], public and private – failed to cohere; with many government representatives refusing to start negotiations in the presence of civil society representatives. Eventually a declaration was prepared, reading like something of a conceptual hybrid between the Declaration of the Rights of Man, the American Declaration of Independence, the Kyoto Agreement, and the introduction to Star Trek: Again the conflation of an understanding of contemporary reality with specification and aspiration.

We, the representatives of the peoples of the world, assembled in Geneva from 10-12 December 2003 for the first phase of the World Summit on the Information Society, declare our common desire and commitment to build a people-centred, inclusive and development-oriented Information Society, where everyone can create, access, utilize and share information and knowledge, enabling individuals, communities and peoples to achieve their full potential in promoting their sustainable development and improving their quality of life, premised on the purposes and principles of the Charter of the United Nations and respecting fully and upholding the Universal Declaration of Human Rights. (WSIS, 2003)

We the digital people ... ?

One commentator (Larsen, 2003) affirmed that the summit was called to 'create ways of bridging the global *digital divide*'; and then posed the question – 'But will its political tensions and complex agenda make it less of an "internet-Kyoto" and more of an arid talk shop?' Rather ignoring the fact that Kyoto is seen by many as itself little more than an arid talk shop.

The official – i.e. government and business – WSIS declaration reflected the view that WSIS is more like the WTO than UNESCO; and certainly nothing like the peoples' forum that many of the civil society participants had envisaged. Thus the declaration did little to disrupt the commercial status-quo; it was a call for on-line business as usual, with perhaps a few new provisos. The civil society groups were eventually locked-out of several sessions and so opted to produce their own declaration of principles. Whereas the official declaration focused on themes similar to those in the Bangemann report and the like, the civil society one centred on themes far more akin to The Bandung declaration. The official report is couched in terms of market orientation, recognition of intellectual property rights and so on; whereas the civil society report focuses on the necessity to re-evaluate power and relationships, issues of personal integrity and accountability. The official declaration of principles from WSIS is entitled *Building the Information Society: a global challenge in the new Millennium*; the WSIS Civil Society declaration (2003) is entitled *Shaping Information Societies for Human Needs*. The former reads like an early specification for a major (corporately financed?) construction project; the latter more of a political appeal for the initiation of new – trans-national – social processes.

The outcomes from WSIS 2003 exemplify the range of contending and contentious issues surrounding the current social context – its potentialities, its proclivities, its portents. It also adds weight to the argument that contributing to the development of Haraway's concept of informatics is necessary and urgent.

The official WSIS declaration, confident and mechanistic in tone, resonates with Bell and the info-utopians; the NGO declaration is far less certain of the beneficial effects of existing trends on poverty, equality, justice, and human rights. The political and corporate elite have taken Bell and his ilk as their avatar, but Bell's ideas must be seen more as symptom than as analysis. In any case in terms of analytic content and portent, Bell's work has now been surpassed by Castells'.

To an important extent Castells builds on Bell's work and makes numerous references to it, although one of the ironies is that Castells' own formation was profoundly influenced by his contact with and participation in the May 1968 political upheavals in Europe. One of the key claims of the activists and theorists of '68 was that the traditional working class was disappearing, and would be replaced by a new revolutionary – ideological – class based on educated workers and professional groups, an argument which Bell specifically challenged and sought to discredit. But there is crucial distinction between Bell and Castells in their characterization and analysis of the fundamental bases of the new social contexts. Where Bell argues that capitalism has been transcended, Castells argues that what he terms *informationalism* is itself a form of capitalism, albeit a specific and unique one ...

> information, in its broadest sense, e.g. as communication of knowledge, has been critical in all societies ... In contrast, the term informational indicates the attribute of a specific form of social organization in which information generation, processing, and transmission become fundamental sources of productivity and power, because of new technological conditions emerging in this historical period. (1996, p21)

The developments from Bell's work to Castells' extended analysis of the network society must form a cornerstone of informatics, and it is encouraging to note that within the IS academy and elsewhere there are a whole series of discussions and analyses emanating from these key resources. As such there is little excuse for permitting the usually taken-for-granted and therefore unspecified sophomoric sociology that many have been allowed to get away with in their pronouncements on contemporary society in the context of ICT.[52]

---

52 Langdon Winner (*The Whale and the Reactor* – chapter 9) refers to the phenomenon encapsulated by 'brandy and cigars and human values' – i.e. the time when those with the wealth and power ponder crucial topics such as 'human values' such as justice, equality and the like; but

The work of those such as Bell and Castells is important, but needs to be understood within a more profound sociological context. There is some recognition of this, and within the IS academy most frequent and popular recourse has been to the work of Giddens – specifically his work on structuration and the analysis of contemporary society outlined in his 1999 Reith Lectures (1999); and there is also a developing body of work derived from Latour, particularly his actor-network theory (1987).

Whatever the specific resources and concepts that are employed, the ultimate aim has to be to encourage people to 'think informatically'; to adapt another of Bauman's phrases. We have to begin to understand the specific nature of the 'biological, social, linguistic and cultural changes' to which our attention is drawn as the source, nature and limitations of technicism, and the full extent and complexities of informatics become apparent. This demands that we have to make a start on conceiving of society in terms that move beyond the confines and misconceptions of the modernist and mechanist orientations that are all too common and unquestioningly accepted across all disciplines; and as has already been stated, but will be further demonstrated later in this chapter, it is with the work of Bauman himself that we can most profitably begin. (NB Giddens himself acknowledged that his concept of 'structuration' was derived from Bauman's work in *Culture as Praxis*, in which Bauman himself develops ideas from Levi-Strauss – originally published in 1973.)

It is, however, vital to understand that the necessity for such *abnormal* discourse is not a demand that can be satisfied in a once-and-for-all fashion. The inadequacies of mechanistic and technicist orientations and beliefs will not suddenly lie exposed for all to see. The cognitive misconceptions at the root of mechanistic and technicist thinking, or what Ellul has more appropriately termed *technique*, are never tracked back to this orientation itself; but on the contrary are

---

with only the remotest possibility that such weighty considerations will actually amount to a great deal of insight, and no chance that it will actually influence what they do in their day-time occupations.

usually explained as deriving from inadequate application of technology. The posited solution is always seen as more-of-the-same. Illich (2001) highlighted this paradox, particularly with regard to medicine, where he introduced the term *iatrogenic*, encapsulating his argument that the development of modern (highly technicized and professionalized) medicine results in far higher rates of illness, sickness and disease. Modern medical practices result in a coalescence of interested parties bent on high rates of intervention and medicalization of all sickness. This leads to increased dependence on doctors and the medical and caring professions in general, accompanied by loss of control on the part of non-professionals who can only take on the role of (passive, patient) patients; consumers of health care services. Furthermore this concentration of treatment in hospitals, accompanied by increased intervention and testing leads to higher incidences of identified maladies as well as creating new ones, sometimes caused by the treatment and medical processes themselves. So modern medical practices become self-perpetuating and self-generating; responding to needs and demands which can never be satisfied since they in turn give rise to still further ailments, demands for preventative treatments and so on.

To illustrate the point that this exposure of the limitations of technicism is never once-and-for-all, but must constantly be reiterated and restated, consider the use of Illich's term *iatrogenic*. The term has itself now been largely appropriated by the medical profession to apply to illness caused, in a very direct sense, by treatment or hospitalization. Thus side-effects of drugs or MRSA[53] are classed as iatrogenic, but with the assumption that they can be treated or prevented by further medical interventions. This medical-mechanistic appropriation of Illich's concept demonstrates the continuing power of technicism. A concept that ought to result in a substantive critique of medicalization is re-defined and drafted in to bolster precisely what it was meant to expose and subvert.

---

53 MRSA stands for 'methicillin resistant Staphylococcus aureus', but is also the acronym used with reference to the general category of 'superbugs' which proliferate in hospitals with dire and often fatal results.

Ellul and Bauman both give the wider – and more insidious and pervasive – context to this. Ellul in his characterization of the technological system as self-generating and self-perpetuating, and Bauman in his imagery of flow and movement totally lacking in direction or objective. To apply Illich's ideas in a wider context, this is a *technological* nemesis, where technology has become *technogenic* – technology now engendering new needs, new demands and new impetus for novelty and innovation. This can be termed techno-genesis; technical innovations that feed on themselves.

What we have is a situation that has moved beyond the analyses of Williams and Winston. There is no longer any braking to balance the technological accelerator. Technology has become a motive force in and of itself, so that anything that can be 'invented' will be invented and marketed as the latest innovation – in a long and endless line of such novelty. In some cases inventions will be developed as solutions to problems that do not yet exist, but which will be discovered or concocted once there is a solution at hand.

Moreover we need to be able to locate these features socially; but where is the social theory that begins to characterize and explain the genesis and trajectory of this *techno-genic* and *praxeomorphic* milieu? The context within which these developments are taking place can best be understood with reference to Bauman's recent work, and in particular his concept of *Liquid Modernity*. Bauman's recent writings all focus on the notion of *liquid modernity*, a term he introduced beginning in the late 1990s, initially in his deceptively short, but conceptually immense books on *Globalization* and *Community*. The concept was then developed in subsequent works such as *In Search of Politics* and most specifically in *Liquid Modernity*. But there is an important continuity with his early work, particularly *Legislators and Interpreters* (1987). There are many key aspects of this work that are of particular importance in seeking to develop informatic thinking, but at this point it is one of his concluding remarks that is most pertinent.

We have seen that the rationalization process has brought in its wake an extreme fragmentation of the sites of authority; in each site, *availability of rational technology permits an ever increasing measure of autonomy from the system, leaving the market as the only link between sites.* Thus rationalization of the fragments of the system does not lead to the rationality of the system as a totality. (Bauman, 1987, p188 stress added)

In this book, dating from 1987, many of the key themes of liquid modernity are prefigured. The idea that rationalization is a process of fragmentation rather than integration is central to Bauman's argument; as is the description of the state as an 'instrument of re-commodification', acting in concert with a market that subsumes legitimation and social integration, resulting in radical individualization. This resonates with the individualization thesis of Beck & Beck-Gernsheim (2001), but predates it by several years.

In his writings from the early 1990s – his emeritus period – he has focused on the concepts of ambivalence and fluidity; culminating in his particular concept of *liquid modernity*. Some have described Bauman as the key theorist of post-modernism, but his most recent works have dispensed with this term entirely in favour of *liquid modernity*. In fact Bauman has always maintained a distance from identifying post-modernism with a new way of studying (social) reality; one of his now classic epithets is that there is no post-modern sociology, but there needs to be a sociology of post-modernism (1992).

Bauman sets the stage for his characterization of liquid modernity in his preceding works that themselves characterize the project of modernity. For Bauman one of the central features of modernity was founded on its distrust of any spontaneous emergence of community; 'the sole conceivable order was an order designed using the power of reason and maintained by day-to-day monitoring and management' (p38, 1993). Thus the distrust took the dual form of simultaneously assuming that no conceivable order could emerge without management and monitoring, and that any form of organization that did emerge without such supervision could not be allowed to flourish.

The inherent, but ambivalent, relationship between modernity and management is a recurring theme in Bauman's work. The paradox and ambivalence of autonomy and heteronomy are central to his writings from the late 1980s to the present; and if there is one redeeming feature of our current liquid modern times, then perhaps Bauman might point to the way in which the forces of liquid modernity have brought about the end to any comfortable and unchallenged symbiosis between modernity and heteronomy, with a concomitant lowering of the distrust of spontaneity. (This symbiosis can be defined as 'any of several living arrangements between members of two different species, including mutualism, commensualism, and parasitism'!)

> The state-legislated morality and the diffuse moral pressures
> of the self-appointed spokesmen of postulated communities are
> unanimous on one point: they both deny or at least curtail the
> individual moral discretion. (1993, p46)

Bauman quotes from *The Communist Manifesto* to summarize the classic agenda of what he would now insist we recognize as the first stage of modernity; evoking a project aimed at dismantling the old, traditional and solid so that it could and would be replaced by the new, the modern.

> *All fixed, fast frozen relations, with their train of ancient and*
> *venerable prejudices and opinions, are swept away, all new-*
> *formed ones become antiquated before they can ossify. All*
> *that is solid melts into air, all that is holy is profaned, and*
> *man is at last compelled to face with sober senses his real*
> *condition of life and his relations with his kind.*
> *The need of a constantly expanding market for its products*
> *chases the bourgeoisie over the entire surface of the globe. It*

must nestle everywhere, settle everywhere, establish connections everywhere.

But as Bauman points out this conquest of the fluid over the stagnant was, for first-stage modernists, only to be a means for establishing a new solidity – a brave new world where the inherited set of deficient and defective solids would be replaced by a much improved and preferably perfect set, 'and for that reason no longer alterable'. But this process of un-freezing proved to be unstoppable; like the sorcerer's apprentice, our predecessors unleashed a chain of events that feed upon themselves and propagate unrelentingly. The breaking up of old forms never ends, there is a constant flow and movement. This is not post-modernity; it has not gone beyond modernity. On the contrary it is the undiluted and inescapable form of modernity itself: Liquid Modernity; what in Joycean terms we might call *the ineluctable modality of the fluid.* His earlier work on *Postmodern Ethics* (1993) can be seen as preparatory to the later work, although in this earlier statement modernity is seen less as liquid and more as self-dismantling or self-disassembly.

It must be noted that Bauman avoids the elisions of which Bell and many others are guilty. He rejects the concept of *post*-anything, and also resists any tendency to speculate about or offer specifications for the future. Hence he avoids any criticisms of conflating 'is' with 'ought', or of confusing his analysis of the present with his hopes for the future. Yet by so doing he has attracted criticisms that point to his failure to offer any solutions or recommendations. His response is often to quote Hannah Arendt; 'I am not duty bound to resolve the difficulties I create'[54].

Bauman rejects the label *post*-modern since this implies something above and beyond what went before; on the contrary, Bauman wishes to stress that social

---

[54] The original is in fact from Lessing as quoted by Arendt and used by Bauman, who clarified this in a recent conversation.

processes are a continuation and intensification of those underlying modernity itself. Hence he gives an approving mention to Ulrich Beck's term of 'Second Modernity'. Thus Bauman's analyses of society, politics, culture, individualization and the like chronicle an accelerating process of decomposition and flux; and in his recent writings he develops this theme with reference to concepts such as emancipation, individuality, time/space, work, community, and identity.

In this second or liquid phase, modernity's melting powers have now spread and intensified so that earlier reference points and concepts, presumed to be fixed and immutable, have been emptied of meaning and content. Beck in his analysis of *second modernity*, has spoken of zombie categories and zombie institutions, for example *family, class, neighbourhood*. Bauman develops this insight by noting that we have a 'redistribution and reallocation of modernity's *melting powers*' (2000, p6). Initially aimed at 'extant institutions' these melting powers have now moved on to undermine 'configurations, constellations, patterns of dependency and interactions'. 'The liquidizing powers have moved from the *system* to *society*, from *politics* to *life-policies*' – so that they now liberate everything from the macro to the micro level of 'social cohabitation'. This release is not liberating in an invigorating or cathartic sense, since individuals have continually and continuously to recreate and reinvent themselves, re-assembling their own biography. This parallels Sennett's recent writings (2000) which illustrate the point that although routine employment may be boring, it is less enervating than constantly having to re-invent oneself and one's life-context. Following a script may become dull and unexciting, but it takes a great deal less effort than having constantly and continually to write and rewrite and act out one's own script, and do it differently each day.

As Bauman encapsulates it, this phase of social development 'sets itself no objective and draws no finishing line; ... it assigns the quality of permanence solely to the state of transience. Time *flows* – it no longer marches on'. This is akin to Kafka's tale – *My Destination* – in which there is journey, but indeed no obvious and known destination.

> I called for my horse to be brought from the stable. The servant did not understand me. I myself went into the stable, saddled my horse and mounted. In the distance I heard a trumpet blast. I asked him what it meant but he did not know and had not heard it.
>
> By the gate he stopped me and asked "where are you riding to sir?"
>
> I answered "away from here, away from here, always away from here. Only by doing so can I reach my destination."
>
> "Then you know your destination" he asked.
>
> "Yes" I said "I have already said so, 'Away-From-Here' that is my destination."
>
> "You have no provisions with you" he said.
>
> "I don't need any" I said. "The journey is so long that I will die of hunger if I do not get something along the way. It is, fortunately, a truly immense journey." (nd)

Since the late 1990s Bauman has developed his ideas in the context of politics, individualization, society, globalization, and community. His concept of liquid modernity is now an established component of contemporary sociology, and discussion of any aspect of ICT, informatics, or to use Bauman's words '*availability of rational technology*', demands some engagement with his ideas. He offers few direct references to technology, but in general ICT as characterized in the previous chapters forms a backdrop to Bauman's work rather than a specific topic of extended analysis.

The metaphor of liquidity and flow underlines the point that this *liberation* from solidity and control is double-edged; it removes the constraints of the past, but does not supply new ones.[55] Thus 'patterns of dependency and interaction' need 'attention, constant vigilance and perpetual effort – and even then the success of the effort is anything but a foregone conclusion'. Bauman is well aware that this state of affairs is paradoxical – indeed it is something that he stresses. The idea of sweeping away, of constant change and transformation can equally apply to what replaces the fixed, fast frozen relations – and this is exactly what Bauman's liquid modernity highlights; it is just like the dictionary entry for the word 'iteration' which simply states 'see iteration'.[56]

The word *liquidity* evokes the imagery of flow, and of constant movement and change. Flow results in erosion and deposition of waste and debris, and Bauman follows this imagery in his recent work – particularly *Wasted Lives*. Here Bauman offers the obverse of Bell's utopianism; the liquid present produces waste, detritus and refuse, some of it in human form. Liquid modern society is not one in which we can all happily do business with each other with a universal win-win outcome. It is an *unfitness landscape* where fortified encampments and gated communities exist in not-too-close proximity with waste dumps, transit camps and service zones.

One key effect of this momentum is that the concept of routine, previously seen as a burden on creativity and enhancement, now takes on a more positive and reassuring meaning. Stability and certainty may be tedious, but they may also be far less stressful than not knowing what tomorrow will bring, and knowing that whatever does appear will itself be transitory. This nostalgia for the mundane is particularly applicable to people's employment and self-development. Apart from a very few professions, the possibility of a career, in the sense of progression along a more-or-less fixed path from novice to expert, is no longer available.

---

55 In a recent private communication Frank Land, commenting on a draft of this chapter, offered the observation that there are still some points of stability, or at least aspects that are not swept away – e.g. calculation and justification always in terms of maximizing shareholder value.

56 In the 2003 presentation on Liquid Modernity, given together with Zygmunt Bauman, I used the image of a Klein Bottle to evoke this concept – see Bryant et al, 2006.

There is no career ladder to climb; or if there is one, the ladder, as in a circus act, rests with its top in midair, its base balanced precariously on a unicycle. Shannon's diversionary pastime has become the *modus vivendi* for the liquid modern worker.

> Renowned for his eclectic interests and capabilities— including such activities as juggling while riding a unicycle down the halls of Bell Labs—Shannon produced many provocative and influential articles on information theory, cryptography, and chess-playing computers, as well as designing various mechanical devices. (Obituary for Claude Shannon)

So in the era of liquid modernity there is no comfort or shelter of last resort in concepts or realities associated with *community, society, identity, family* etc. Similarly there is no consolation that there will be some utopian end-point to the process of direction-less flow. Indeed the only objective is flow itself. Bauman states that one cannot even ask 'towards what?' The movement is the objective itself, there is no other. Bauman offers a profound pessimism or perhaps a challenge, and he refers to Stevenson's assertion that it is better to travel hopefully than it is to arrive. But what if we are travelling hopelessly?[57]

So we are like those cartoon characters hurtling over a cliff or sailing over Niagara Falls, but continuing horizontally in a straight line and only falling once we look down and see there is nothing to support us: Or in this case, only becoming aware of our predicament once we read Bauman. Bauman suggests that one thing that might prevent us falling is our speed, or using Virilio's term *speed-space*; and Bauman also alludes to Emerson's dictum that when skating over thin ice, speed is the only form of safety.

---

57 In a presentation in 2003 (Bryant et al, 2006) the person introducing Professor Bauman stated that he was 'not a Jeremiah', at which point Professor Bauman turned to me and proudly said 'See, I am not a Jeremiah' – but I suspect Jeremiah might have said the same thing about himself.

Yet this speed cannot be maintained indefinitely. At some point something has to give. We will run out of space or speed-space, or we will exhaust our energy or other resources. As Marx noted in a pointed dig at Feuerbach, to suppose otherwise would be like arguing that 'someone could resist drowning by resisting the idea of gravity'. Admittedly gravity only has meaning in relation to something solid, and certainly only something with mass; but it resonates with Bauman's contention that there are no such solid points where we can land and from which we can orient ourselves. We should forget any quest for certainty based on solidifying the past or the present or the future-just-around-the-corner. So appeals to *traditional values, what we have and where we are now*, or *just one more transition* have no validity – they all rely on a mechanical, solid world view.

Bauman's sustained and extended imagery of liquidity and fluidity is inherently also bound up with speed. It would be more comforting if it were bound up with velocity, since that at least incorporates direction; but Bauman excludes any such consolation. We can, however, develop the metaphor of flux and flow, bearing in mind the role of metaphor as discussed in chapter 3. We can say that as the speed of flow increases this flow can become turbulent; at which point classic models of fluid dynamics simply breakdown in the face of the unknowable, unpredictable, uncontrollable. So is the end point of liquid modernity a spiralling down into a vortex? Is our eventual destination a metaphorical plug-hole? If first modernity is the all-too-solid Scylla – initially beautiful and now revealed as monstrous; then liquid modernity is the all-too-fluid Charybdis – aimlessly voracious.

If the flux of liquid modernity leads to turbulence as the speed of flow increases, is there any way in which we can respond other than simply being swept along? Bauman's books in recent years appear to provide an argument for the complete dismantling of customary or time-honoured forms of intervention and political or group action. He offers an extended analysis and diagnosis, but without any prescription of palliative. Again the contrast with Bell is instructive.

Bell's work is symptomatic, advocating that we can and should all go along for the ride. Bauman on the other hand is profound and analytic, pointing out that we are all going along for the ride whether we like it not. And so we are all left with a puzzle. How can we start to understand the possibilities and appropriate modes of action in such a context? If we are living in liquid modern times, potentially or actually turbulent modern times, we need some ways of grasping the nature of this new reality. Following Haraway we need to develop our understanding of the *technologies of information and communication as well as the biological, social, linguistic and cultural changes that initiate, accompany and complicate their development.* Furthermore we need to search for some ways in which we can exert a modicum of control in such circumstances.

Turbulence has been defined by Robert Rosner, an eminent professor both of physics and astronomy, as a 'real-life exhaustive problem' that perplexes researchers, and is well beyond their predictive abilities (quoted in Stewart, 2002). Not only are they unable to understand – i.e. model, control, predict – the details of things such as explosions of neutron stars or the behaviour inside nuclear reactors; they are equally stumped in understanding what happens when you stir your milk into your coffee. So turbulence at the social level will be several orders of magnitude harder to grasp. This should be seen, however, as a challenge rather than another reason for despair.

Bauman's concept of liquidity, involving self-motivating and self-perpetuating flux and flow, evokes similarities with the concept of *turbulent fields* in the work of Emery & Trist from the 1960s (1965). In their work at the Tavistock in the 1960s, they distinguished between four types of *causal texture* – placid-randomized, placid-clustered, disturbed-reactive, turbulent. Placid-randomized causal textures or environments, are characterized by 'goals and noxiants (*goods* and *bads*) [that] are relatively unchanging in themselves and randomly distributed'. This corresponds to 'the economist's classical market'. In such causal textures, there is no distinction between tactics and strategy; and tactics can be learned by simple trial and error, and then generalized across the entire environment. The placid-randomized environment sounds more of an idealized context than anything that might exist, but Emery & Trist exemplify it in ecological terms as a large area of grassland, such as the Steppes, where vast barren expanses are punctuated by small concentrations of food.

The placid-clustered environment differs from the randomized one, since 'goals and noxiants are not randomly distributed but hang together in certain ways'; likened by Emery & Trist to 'imperfect competition' or Ashby's 'serial systems'. Strategy and tactics are now distinct since it becomes important to be able to decipher the non-uniform environment, gaining an understanding of which parts to avoid and which to approach. The ecological example they offer would be an area of scrub land with clearings and forested areas; the latter being both sources of danger from attack as well as food and shelter. Since the main focus of Emery & Trist's work was organizational design and development, they also pointed out that organizations in such contexts develop long-term plans and devise resource management strategies accordingly. This also necessitates the development and encouragement of (vertical and horizontal) division of labour or 'distinctive competences', accompanied by centralization and hierarchy aimed at optimizing co-ordination and control.

The third type of causal texture is termed disturbed-reactive; and is likened to Ashby's ultra-stable system or in economic terms to an oligopolic market. The key difference between this texture and the previous one is that as well as the environmental aspects, account has to be taken of other, significant competitors. So strategies involve anticipating the actions of others and also anticipating their anticipations, and so on. Emery & Trist also point out that as well as tactics and strategy, the concept of *operations* is also required. This brings together 'a planned series of tactical initiatives, calculated reasons by others, and counter-actions'. One key ramification of this additional facet is that some de-centralization is required since there is a 'premium on quality and speed of decision at various peripheral points'.

This assumption is based on the derivation of *operations* from the military context, where the lack of any, or any reliable, real-time communications necessitates decentralization of this sort. Organizations have to decide on the extent to which they are prepared to decentralize; although in the context of an information society – or an informational one – it might now be thought possible to overcome this dilemma with the introduction of reliable real-time communications and monitoring.

Organizations have to choose between strategies that range from the fiercely competitive to the openly co-operative; and will have to judge when to move across this range. Ecologically this can be likened to an environment with several groups of chimpanzees, in close proximity to baboons, leopards, etc. – so there is co-location of competitors and predators. This is a context of an oligopoly with non-zero sum competition, and so demands that actors foster alliances and out-think competitors. 'One has to know when not to fight to the death'.

The fourth type of causal texture is the turbulent field, and it is this that resonates with Bauman's liquid modernity. Emery & Trist argued that in this context the dynamic processes themselves lead to the triggering of other dynamic processes, some of them emerging from the turbulent field itself. 'The *ground* is in motion.' They allude to the phenomenon of 'soldiers marching in step over a bridge'. Furthermore they also argue that in such contexts there is an 'increasing reliance on research and development ... [leading] to a situation in which a change gradient is continuously present'. This hints at the far more profound ideas of Ellul and Bauman where the nature of the technological system feeds on its own momentum.

Emery & Trist also pointed to the 'deeper interdependence between the economic and other facets of society', which accords with Bauman's point about the pivotal role of the market; although Bauman is far clearer about the unwelcome nature of allowing the market to become the primary factor and site of co-ordination. (The specific mechanisms by which this operates are not a specific focus for Bauman.)

In ecological terms turbulence is exemplified by disrupted eco-systems such as rain-forests in the 20th century, and even more so now in the 21stcentury. It also applies to the current global economic system; 'the dynamic properties arise not simply from the interaction of the component organizations, but also from the field itself. The *ground* is in motion'. There is even a presentiment of Beck's work, when Emery & Trist point out that 'these trends mean a gross increase in ... *relevant uncertainty*. The consequences which flow from ... actions lead off in ways that become increasingly unpredictable: they do not necessarily fall off with distance, but may at any point be amplified beyond all expectation; similarly, lines of action that are strongly pursued may find themselves attenuated by emergent field forces.' (Bauman in *Postmodern Ethics* makes a similar point when discussing the unintended and unimagined consequences of actions, and the development of modern ideas about risk and uncertainty, etc.)

Emery & Trist's prescience emanates from parallels between Bauman's liquid modernity and the development of ideas about complexity and chaos from the systems world. They developed their ideas from the work of early systems theorists such as Ashby (1959), von Bertalanffy (1969), and Churchman (1984). Later developments around the concepts of complexity and chaos developed, in part, from similar influences.

The context detailed so eloquently by Bauman is one in which flow has moved into turbulence, although Bauman himself does not use the term; and turbulence has become endemic, not simply a phase of transition between points of stability or at least non-turbulent flow. Liquid modernity has developed precisely because the sources of change and dynamism that propelled *first modernity* have now produced a *second modernity* that gains its impetus from its own origins and outcomes. It is self-propelling and cannot be grasped using traditional mechanistic concepts of laws, rules, uniformities and their ilk.

Ideas drawn from the work of those seeking to explain and exploit ideas of turbulence, chaos and complexity appear to offer some conceptual value. The mechanistic concepts of first modernity need to be held up against the complex ones of second modernity. Explicitly stated rules and algorithms must be contrasted with strategies that assume that there is no final answer and no basis upon which to arrive at a definitive and calculated solution; although at certain points there may be a 'settling into a condition' – but this will be more-or-less transitory. Any attempt to exert central control will be thwarted by the real complexity of the turbulent texture. Extensive top-down directives may have unforeseen consequences – sometimes contradictory or paradoxical, or no effect at all. On the other hand, small changes may have considerable effects. The concept of command-and-control has to be replaced by genuinely distributed control, with effective empowerment dispersed around the system.

Writing in the 1960s within the context of organizational development, Emery & Trist were clear that the response to turbulent fields cannot be simply a larger, more bureaucratic and over-arching hierarchy. On the contrary, their tentative solution relied not on stronger, more powerful or extensive structures, but on 'the emergence of *values that have overriding significant* (sic!) *for all members of the field*' (stress in original). The justification for this is that in conditions of persistent 'relevant uncertainty', attempting to select a course of action on the basis of its consequences is self-defeating and largely pointless – there is no way of having or developing any insight or understanding of future effects. Thus Emery & Trist suggested that people will need to have recourse to 'rules … to provide them with a guide and ready calculus'. They did not specifically discuss how such rules or values – 'such as the ten commandments' – will emerge and be sustained. They simply offered the imperative statement that strategic objectives can no longer be formulated in terms of location (which apply for clustered fields) or capabilities (appropriate for disturbed fields), but 'must now be formulated in terms of *institutionalisation*'; and they followed Selznick in defining the latter as the state an organization reaches 'through the embodiment of organizational values which relate them to the wider society'.

There are two immense and potentially insurmountable problems with this sort of affirmation. First there is nothing to indicate any ways in which organizational values can become more socially-oriented, and no mention of the significant barriers to any such transition. Second, and more critical in the early 21st century than perhaps in the more solid 1960s, is that the values of liquid modern society are themselves precisely those of the turbulent causal texture. Hence Bauman's admonitory tone. Emery & Trist may have hoped that their prescription would lead to a calming effect; pouring oil on troubled waters. Unfortunately there is no oil, only still more agitated waters.

A more profound issue is one on which Bauman, and many sociologists in general, part company from the utopian neutralism (neutral utopianism?) of Emery & Trist, and many other systems theorists. Emery & Trist see society and the state as ultimate arbiters and the source of safety, security and sagacity; hence their recourse to 'institutionalisation and the wider society'. Bauman points precisely to institutions as the problem rather than the solution. In *Postmodern Ethics* they occupy a neutral but anomalous position.

> Through these arrangements, the organization does not promote immoral behaviour. It does not sponsor evil, as some of its critics would hasten to charge; yet it does not promote good either … It simply renders social action *adiaphoric* (the term *adiaphoron* belongs to the language of *ecclesia*; it meant originally a belief or a custom declared by the Church indifferent – neither merit nor sin – and hence requiring … no official endorsement or prohibition) (Bauman, 1993, p125)

In his Liquid Modernity writings even this dispassionate foundation has been swept away by the incessant flow to nowhere.

Yet not all those drawing attention to this turbulent, uncertain environment see it as unwelcome and threatening. There are many who employ the imagery of speed, turbulence and uncertainty in affirmative terms. Thus people point to the value of upheaval and turbulence when there is the need to alter the present state of affairs; for instance if there is too much power concentrated in the hands of the state, or where there is too much stability, stasis and resistance. Advocates, as likely to come from the old left as from the new right, often unwittingly use the imagery of the youthful Marx and Engels, proclaiming the need to sweep away the old order, making way for the new. Whatever they may envisage as their specific alternative it is always a *new order* that will displace the old one. They fail to understand that the processes of liquid modernity, once unleashed, cannot be controlled and rationally managed. This applies to many governments and states. They have moved from dreams of overall control and authority to protestations of hands-off administration and allowing the market free rein – or free reign. To a large extent this has been a simple recognition of the inevitable, rather than a conscious and deliberate choice. The state, founded on the tripod of military, economic and cultural sovereignty, now finds that all three legs have been broken, the economic most of all. Yet the dominant theme from the 1980s onwards has been that governments have not simply advocated a hands-off stance, but have actively encouraged *flow*, *flux*, and *freedom*; using slogans such as deregulation, privatization, outsourcing, and market testing, which all too often move out of control and become turbulent. This is like the sorcerer's apprentice, unleashing forces that cannot be controlled, and which appear to be beyond anyone's or any group's power. But there is no sorcerer who can break the spell; and the role of the apprentice has been usurped by the putative 'experts' – the modern day apprentices who like to think of themselves as sorcerers.[58]

---

58 Bauman sketches this scenario, and fills in many of the details in his recent work. Yet his earlier work offers perhaps some indication of a way in which we can break out of this morass; hence his discussion of concepts of autonomy and morality; and a renewed or rediscovered role for legislators.

154

Bauman's analysis of liquid modernity is potentially pessimistic, despite his protestations. It may also be quietist and quiescent. To paraphrase New Labour's slogan of the mid-1990s, the maxim for liquid modern times is 'things can only get *different'*, and will do so regardless of any human intervention. Indeed on one interpretation of the concepts of turbulence and complexity, any plans for developing major interventions and grand strategies are doomed to failure. We are in a realm of unpredictability: We are not quite 'up salt creek without a paddle', but at best we are trying to paddle against a current that is far stronger than our best efforts, even than our collective best efforts. Perhaps the only option is to go with the flow, although we have no idea where it will lead.

Once the fluidity of modernity is taken into account, one central and common agenda item must be seen as having only a tenuous claim for inclusion – the idea that because things are moving out-of-control we need to find ways in which more control can be exerted. In *Postmodern Ethics*, which predates but anticipates his development of liquid modernity, Bauman avers that whereas 'the moral thought and practice of modernity was animated by the belief in the possibility of a *non-ambivalent, non-aporetic code'*, postmodernity represents the '*disbelief* in such a possibility' (stress in original).[59]

In a more general sense, the project of modernity is to resolve all ambiguity and ambivalence; the darkness of confusion being gradually completely replaced with the light of reason, which garners universal consent. What post-modernity does is to point out that as the light of reason sweeps across one terrain, in its wake it leaves previously enlightened areas in the shadows. So there is an important distinction between first (solid) and second (liquid) modernity. Building on Bauman's work, liquid modernity undermines any basis for the belief that, given time and resources, science and technology will provide the basis for engineered solutions to all manner of problems. On the contrary, we have to understand that any 'solutions' are simply problems waiting to happen, or to be

---

59 *Aporia* – sceptical, unbelieving; *aporiai* – the Greek word for puzzles

recognized as such. Yet this is a state in which no-one can feel comfortable; there is a constant urge to 'take control'. Bauman leaves his readers with this paradox, but that is not a position in which we can remain; part of our condition is precisely not to be satisfied with such paradoxical impotence.

In recent times there have been concerted efforts by some to develop a conceptual grasp of turbulence and unpredictability; and to model it, often taking advantage of the enormous increases in computing power. Some of these efforts go under the name of theories of chaos or complexity – and include terms such as fitness landscapes, strange attractors, etc. A useful introduction to the whole area can be found in Gleick's book *Chaos*.

> Where chaos begins, classical science stops. For as long as the world has had physicists inquiring into the laws of nature, it has suffered a special ignorance about disorder in the atmosphere, in the turbulent sea, in the fluctuations of wildlife populations, in the oscillations of the heart and brain. The irregular side of nature, the discontinuous and erratic side – these have been puzzles to science, or worse, monstrosities. (1988, p3)

Given the earlier observations relating the turbulent causal texture of Emery & Trist to Bauman's and Ellul's arguments, perhaps something from work on complexity and chaos can be harnessed to help us understand or come to terms with liquid modernity: Even if we must accept that the concept of total or increasing control is a delusion. If, however, we do use such work we must be aware that it will involve transpositions from the physical and mathematical world to the social one; and so there must be a considerable and flamboyant health warning. (Indeed one of Bauman's earlier works specifically castigated sociologists for erecting a 'second nature' standing as some 'irremovable component of human experience which defies human will and sets unencroachable limits to human action' – (Bauman, 1976, p1).

Moreover any attempts to apply these ideas will encounter scepticism since many people find the concepts and ramifications of chaos and complexity difficult to comprehend and accept; even those who work as scientists. This is hardly surprising since traditional *scientific thinking* – in the sense of a practice contributing to the project aimed at eventual and total understanding and control of reality – is viewed by many as firmly associated with and rooted in pristine, solid modernity. The stereotypical scientific-rationalist would be quite happy with this inexorable link; the post-modernist would point to the same combination as indicative of the failed universalism of all three projects – science, rationalism, modernity. For those still firmly wedded to the promise of solid modernity, much time and effort is still spent looking for linear causal models, a predictive calculus, a set of secure and complete algorithms. Many of those concerned with IS/IT/computing are lured by the mechanical hard-wired promise of technology (which after all was specifically based on *solid*-state physics) as the eventual answer to everything.[60] Although even here there are glimpses of new ways of thinking that are more in line with liquidity than solidity.

The overall impact and generic importance of theories about chaos, and complexity are still unclear and almost by definition, indeterminate; but there is certainly some basis for the view that what at first sight appears to be a complete absence of patterns, networks, structures, and the like is more ordered on closer examination – although whether it is a basis for predictability and control is another matter.

More critically for the context of liquid modernity, chaotic systems can still be *deterministic*, in that any future state of the system might be dependent only on the initial conditions and some equations describing the change of the system with time. It may, however, require 'arbitrarily high precision actually to

---

60 As everyone now knows, thanks to Douglas Adams and *The Hitch-Hiker's Guide to the Galaxy*, there is an answer to everything – it is 42.

calculate a future state to within some finite precision'. In other words, it may not be possible to make the calculation – even with high powered computers. This is because chaotic systems are *dynamically unstable* – which appears to make them unpredictable. So perhaps we do have to reconcile ourselves to the (Bob) Dylanesque stance of simply watching the river flow.

Yet two main components of chaos theory are that systems, no matter how complex they may be, rely upon an underlying order; and that very simple or small changes and events can cause very complex behaviours or perturbations. This latter idea is sometimes stated as *sensitive dependence on initial conditions*, a phenomenon discovered by Edward Lorenz (generally credited as the first experimenter in the area of chaos) in the early 1960s. Lorenz is the person who first introduced the idea that we now term 'the butterfly effect'. The following extract from John H. Lienhard, author and voice of *The Engines of Our Ingenuity*, explains the concept and its ramifications

Author James Gleick tells about MIT meteorologist Edward Lorenz. In 1960 Lorenz tried to model the weather. He wrote simplified equations and solved them on a primitive computer. Sure enough, his output did behave a lot like real weather. His colleagues watched over his shoulder. They were fascinated.

One day, Lorenz tried to continue a run he'd done the day before. He restarted it halfway through. He put in a number from the first run. The output started out just the way it had the day before. Then it began to diverge, crazily.

The equations were the same. The starting point was the same. But the results diverged. Lorenz checked his computer. He checked his arithmetic. Nothing had changed. Same equations, but on subsequent days the results diverged.

There was one difference, but how could it matter? Lorenz rounded off the fourth decimal place of the starting number on the second day. So he stopped to consider. All weather predictions do what his program just did. You can predict the weather for the day after tomorrow. Stretch that to a week, and your prediction always departs from reality.

The implication was staggering. We've always presumed that if you barely change a cause, you'll barely change the effect. Suddenly, Lorenz saw that the weather would change utterly if you started things out just a little differently.

No wonder real weather is so unpredictable! Weather obeys physical laws. But if you change one breath of air, those laws will spin out in a wholly different story.

Meteorologists began talking about something they called the *Butterfly Effect*. The idea was that if a butterfly chances to flap his wings in Beijing in March, then, by August, hurricane patterns in the Atlantic will be completely different. Not long after that day in 1960, the scientific world began changing. Perhaps all kinds of nasty problems we can't solve are nasty just because we can never state them accurately enough.

If this is difficult to comprehend then think instead of a pinball machine, where predicting the path of any one ball is impossible, but where each movement is precisely governed by readily understood laws.

James Gleick has defined chaos/complexity as

a revolution not of technology, like the laser revolution or the computer revolution, but a revolution of ideas. This revolution began with a set of ideas having to do with disorder in nature: from turbulence in fluids, to the erratic flows of epidemics, to the arrhythmic writhing of a human heart in the moments before death.

It has continued with an even broader set of ideas that might be better classified under the rubric of complexity (nd)

And these ideas have spread into the social realm, so that now there is use of chaos and complexity theory by social theorists, economists, therapists and therapeutic communities; also by analysts trying to make sense of the NHS – which involves thinking of the NHS as a turbulent system exhibiting chaos – something that not everyone will find comforting.

There are two attractions in trying to use complexity to understand what we must now agree to call *liquid modernity*. First some seemingly complex, chaotic, random forms of behaviour may be amenable to being understood and modelled by use of a few simple rules and patterns. Thus the behaviour of flocks of birds, or swarms of insects can be explained using only a few simple rules; in the sense that computer models can mimic the behaviour. Perhaps some of the highs and lows of modern economies can be explained in similar fashion – as Joseph Stiglitz (2004) seems to argue; and the same reasoning has been applied to group behaviour such as texting, internet traffic, and swarming or flash-mobs (Howard Rheingold (2003), Mandelbrot & Hudson (2004)).

Second, some theorists of complexity argue that whatever the apparent and potential random nature of any system, order will emerge. Kauffman (2000) has coined the phrase 'order for free', and his explanation of *complex adaptive systems* has been put forward to explain why a seeming infinitude of possibilities does not actually occur and lead to a complete breakdown of order. For instance he argues that the actual possible number of genetic combinations is vast – 10^{30000} – but the actual number of observed combinations, i.e. organisms, is smaller by several orders of magnitude. This he terms 'self-organization', or *order for free*. Although it must be noted that Ashby actually discussed self-organizing systems far earlier, and Prigogine's work (1996) also makes mention of this concept of order emerging from chaos.

Kauffman postulates that just as there are *divergent* systems as demonstrated by Lorenz' work on weather prediction; so too there exist *convergent* ones, arriving at the same end-point even if they have different starting points. Some of his colleagues at The Sante Fe Institute[61] have provided some demonstrations of this at work in various contexts – insect and bacteria growth, avoiding overcrowding at Irish Music nights, stock market behaviour, and more generally in economic systems. As Gleick puts it: 'Life sucks order from a sea of disorder' (1988, p299).[62]

It needs to be noted that Kauffman's phrase 'order for free' is more convoluted and ambivalent than it might appear at first sight. The key point he makes is that some systems, divergent ones, will be sensitive to initial – unpredictable and unavoidable – conditions as Lorenz demonstrated. But others will lead from different starting points to similar conditions; converging to a similar state. These have been termed Kauffman models, random networks exhibiting 'order for free'. Kauffman's main focus is on the fact that such systems do not move into arbitrary states, but exhibit a form of design, or pattern, which can be ascertained and understood in some fashion. He neglects to point out that the term 'order' also has another meaning – implying sequence, hierarchy, stability and control.

Order, in the sense of hierarchy and relative stability, might then be a product – however transient – of dynamic complexity. Moreover this dynamic context might produce different forms of order at different times; so the context is not one of continuous and ubiquitous change, but of sequences and levels of

---

61 See http://www.santafe.edu/

62 One of the key current debates with regard to information systems and IT is between the benefits of the near-monopoly of a single vendor (Microsoft) and the potential offered by open-source software. This latter approach appears at first sight to be a recipe for a disorderly free-for-all – but in practice it seems to exhibit some of the properties of a convergent system. Similarly with other open-source initiatives such as those in the areas of publishing, course development and research collaboration. See Raymond, 2001.

change punctuated by transient stabilities. This then raises the question of the sort of order that emerges from such contexts: Is there some underlying logic or is any ordering simply an accidental outcome?

Liquid modernity may then be amenable to this sort of analysis; but at this juncture I shall not be developing this line of thought any further. This chapter has sought to outline the social context against which our understanding of informatics needs to be embedded. We have a basis to begin to *think informatically*. Before moving on to the concluding chapter it is, however, important that we develop Bauman's recurrent theme and imagery of flux and sweeping away; and in so doing focus on another aspect of liquid modernity to which Bauman has devoted considerable attention. The forces of liquid modernity do not act equally on everyone, nor identically in every place. In his earlier work Bauman contrasted 'tourists' with 'vagabonds'; the idea being that perhaps we are all subjected to forces of liquid modernity, but some – only a very few – can actually harness this energy rather than suffering or enduring its effects. This imagery can be extended so that the category of 'tourist' might be further sub-divided into *Business* and *Steerage* travellers; all on the same journey but with different levels of comfort and use of resources. Upgrades are possible, but unlike air-travel, downgrades are more likely and more numerous. This is the central motif of Bauman's recent work, particularly *Wasted Lives*.

Bauman himself alludes to Nigel Thrift's observations about the changing vocabulary of contemporary business; no longer one of enduring structures but more concerned with flexibility and the ability to transform rapidly in response to unpredictable changes in the environment. Some business gurus have dubbed this the 'Hollywood Model', evoking the process by which a film company is put together from various sources – actors, support staff, directors and producers, technical staff and so on: Naturally obscuring that between films many of the employees have been 'resting' – i.e. temporarily on the waste heap.

But the exponents of new business models and opportunities for consultancy are ready to badge and sell this *management speak*, which includes liquid-like terminology such as 'flexibility', 'coalitions', 'the Hollywood model', virtual teams and organizations, and so on. I suspect it won't be long before some consultancy is selling 'liquid management' on its website – *BauManaging*?

Bauman mentions the advice given by John Kotter – from Harvard Business School – for people not to become entangled in the 'tenure track' form of employment, since designs, concepts, capital, *even knowledge* – stressed by Bauman – have ever decreasing life-spans. If the growing army of short-term, part-time employees had the time or resources – let alone the inclination – to read the proclamations coming out of Harvard Business School they would find little that they didn't already know from bitter experience. Most have no choice even to consider 'tenure track' – i.e. long term employment. Their bitter experience of liquid modernity is the 'freedom' constantly to apply for new jobs – often their existing ones but with 'new conditions' – usually inferior ones (see in particular the recent writings of Ehrenreich, 2001). Kotter's mention of the transience even of 'all kinds of knowledge' also evokes one of the current management fads; *knowledge management*. In cynical terms this can be seen fundamentally to consist of trying to devise computer-based ways of retaining and *leveraging* knowledge without the bother – and cost – of having to retain the people who created it: An attempt to make knowledge really liquid; entirely embodied in software – the definitive liquid asset.

Talk of structures and hierarchies, aims and objectives is passé; only appearing in outmoded institutions (some in the higher education and quality review sectors ruled by the all too solid *audit culture*). But this new vocabulary seems merely to be a veneer; just as re-engineering, down-sizing, right-sizing, and empowerment were euphemisms for redundancy, poorer working conditions, and increased stress in the 1990s. The flow and turbulence of liquid modernity leave a great deal of waste and debris deposited in their wake.

So we have to retain an awareness of the underside of liquid modernity, a reality beneath the veneer – the vagabonds not the tourists; the 50% of adults who have never made a phone call[63], rather than the gee-whizardry of the internet, mobile phones, wearable computers or whatever the next must-have gadget will be. Bauman makes constant reference to this in his work, for instance where he refers to Richard Sennett's observation about the comfort that routine offers, and hence the discomfort of uncertainty. We seem to be caught between the *Hidden Injuries of Class* (Sennett and Cobb's earlier book) and the *Corrosion of Character* (Sennett's revisiting of similar concerns three decades on).

Yet Bauman himself offers no solution – in *Society Under Siege* he pre-empts the question of whether there is 'a way back to a self-confident *agora*', (i.e. 'the space where private problems meet in a meaningful way') or rather a way forward to a new-style *agora*[64] large enough to accommodate the enormity of tasks and responsibilities incubated in a 'company' stretched to the size of the planet?'. As was pointed out in an earlier chapter, his response in place of an answer is to quote Hannah Arendt – 'I am not duty bound to resolve the difficulties I create'.

And he goes on to quote more extensively from Arendt – 'Even in the darkest of times we have the right to expect some illumination that may well come less from theories and concepts than from uncertain, flickering, and often weak light that some men and women, in their lives and their works, will kindle under almost all circumstances and shed over the time span that was given to them on earth.'

Contrasting perhaps with Leszek Kolakowski's defence of the apparent lack of realism of the Solidarity movement in Poland in the early 1980s, that there are situations in which nothing is possible unless you believe that everything is possible.

---

63 Something of a contested figure – but see for instance the work of Clay Shirky, at http://www.shirky.com/writings/half_the_world.html, where he attributes the phrase to Thabo Mbeki in 1996.

64 Agora is now of course a website!

CHAPTER 6
INFORMATICS – DISCIPLINED STRATEGIES FOR DISCIPLINARY COMPLEXITIES

The previous chapters have sought to clarify the contested concepts which comprise ICT – information, communication(s), and technology. The key motivation in dealing with these issues is to lay a basis for the ways in which people can start to think *informatically*: Developing informatics as the study of the availability of rational technologies of information and communication as well as the biological, social, linguistic and cultural changes that initiate, accompany and complicate their development.

Given the content of chapter 1, this raises two key issues: To what extent is this an attempt at developing informatics as a discipline; and what is the relationship between informatics and academic IS[65], and other, related disciplines?

The attempt by Benbasat & Zmud (2003) to develop a prescriptive characterization of information systems as a discipline might be seen as a salutary example of what-not-to-do. Yet the responses their article elicited and provoked have proved enormously useful and constructive in articulating key concepts and features of the flawed discourse that is academic IS. Moreover, some of the responses hint at a remit far wider than even the most *inclusive* definition of academic IS, and so start to resonate with and evoke something akin to informatics as characterized in the preceding pages.

For Bauman, sociology emerged from 'the encounter between the awesome task of the management of organizational processes on a grand, societal scale and the ambitions of the modern state'. This emergence took place against an established disciplinary landscape; and part of this process involved similar

---

65 The term 'Academic IS' is used advisedly, and is used in preference to IS or MIS as it is specifically the academic field that is the key focus in this chapter.

issues of contestation, boundary building and border maintenance with which those embroiled in the newly emerging fields of IS, computing, and informatics have been and still are entangled. Benbasat & Zmud's call for a nomological net to throw around academic IS can be treated as a straw-man of some genuine substance, provoked by the continuing state of fragmented adhocracy that is a core force and compulsion of several emerging and transmogrifying disciplines. Mary Douglas pointed out in *Purity and Danger* (2002) that each of us has a different tolerance of disorder; one person's comfortable and acceptable home or office environment, is someone else's threat and challenge. So too it seems with disciplines. Benbasat & Zmud see chaos and disorder around them, and seek to offer a solution; the imposition of conceptual and organizational tidiness, an ordering of the disorder: But to others the solution is itself a threat and an undermining of what is in fact a fertile and luxuriant terrain. For this latter group, the disciplinary forces and powers-that-be – personified precisely by senior figures such as current or past editors of *MISQ* – threaten the very character and developmental potential of the discipline in all its rich if inchoate variety. The discipline must be un-disciplined; and being a systems-based discipline (see Mason, 2005), those taking issue with Benbasat & Zmud are quick to point to Ashby's law of requisite variety as justification for the current – and not unwelcome – situation.

Ashby's law has been stated as follows – 'The larger the variety of actions available to a control system, the larger the variety of perturbations it is able to compensate.' *Principia Cybernetica*[66]. So on this basis the more *adhocratic* a discipline, the better able it will be to withstand change both from within and without. Thus the recent collection edited by Avgerou et al (2004) embraces and exemplifies the riches within the irregularity and unpredictability within approaches to ICT.

---

66 http://pespmc1.vub.ac.be/REQVAR.html

The aim and continuing objective of requisite variety is not, however, simply acceptance of a conceptual free-for-all. The fragmented adhocracy which is academic IS, and from which informatics may in part emerge, needs to be seen as comprised of a sustained and supported dialogue between a number of *communities of practice* (CoP). The term CoP derives from the work of Lave & Wenger (1991), and can best be understood to refer to collectivities of people who interact with each other, usually in work or professional contexts, and who share or develop common practices in the pursuit of common goals and interests, usually emanating from shared values or principles. Such groups will also tend to pursue similar issues and problems, and express themselves using a common language or terminology.

Academic IS is not a single CoP; it consists of many different, overlapping and contending CoPs. These CoPs will engage with each other in various ways. For the most part the dialogue will be more like a cocktail party, consisting of a variety of conversations and opportunities to eavesdrop on others. At other times it will follow the model of an academic conference or seminar, with different positions and orientations taking turns in a context of congenial discussion and mutual recognition. These exchanges and interchanges may occasionally become more didactic as specific disciplinary and conceptual claims are made, substantiated and challenged. These may be more or less amicable.

The responses evoked by Benbasat & Zmud's article were all couched in supportive and cordial terms, but the collective import was a clear challenge and riposte to any ideas of disciplinary closure and enclosure, and stability based on nomological nets or on anything else. Ives et al (2004) counter what they call Benbasat & Zmud's demand for 'the establishment of an index of paradigmatic conformity', with a model of 'colonial speciation' of disciplinary evolution, derived from Eldredge & Gould's concept of punctuated equilibrium. To paraphrase their argument, they propose that disciplinary fields are best seen as mutually supportive groups learning from each another, but also differentiating themselves from one another and from the 'parent group'. In some cases such sub-groups develop within the main organizational and institutional confines of the discipline – setting up specialist journals, conference tracks, course components and the like. But in other cases, the sub-group flourishes as the main group declines – sometimes with the former taking place at the expense of the latter. Ives et al exemplify this with their account of the emergence of academic IS itself. In part it developed from within what they term 'management sciences', but they also acknowledge that 'many members of our colony came from backgrounds including accounting, computer science, library science, and management'. Their whole argument is couched in terms of 'phylogeny and power', essentially arguing that disciplines cannot be seen in terms of core principles or core concepts without also taking into account the issues of power and control – in part echoing Bauman's argument about the emergence and sustainability of disciplines. They offer a brief account of the generic strategy, of which the recommendations of Benbasat & Zmud are a recent example, using Actor Network Theory (ANT)

> ANT pays attention to how, in a scientific field, established ideas, methods, and techniques are open to controversy and how, after various bargaining and power moves, a negotiated solution becomes institutionalized. As new ideas emerge and then become institutionalized, they turn into a source of disciplinary power and control. They do so by providing the criteria for determining what is being researched, what is being published and, as a consequence, who are to be members of the scientific community in question.

This is broadly in line with the ideas from Bauman and Foucault described in chapter 1. Disciplines are developed as social constructs, and have then continuously to sustain themselves. There will be pressures from within the putative boundary as well as from without. Bauman makes it clear that a discipline such as sociology will find it harder to resist pressures from without than will a resource-dependent, specialist-controlled discipline such as nuclear physics. Academic IS is similarly open to external pressures: The core topics are an uneasy amalgam of pre-existing concerns from various older disciplines together with new issues and concepts that are themselves open to contestation. Other existing disciplines are continually laying claim to some of these concepts, and there is what, following Markus (1999), can be called the problem of ubiquity – ICT, computers, whatever are everywhere, and appear to be everyone's concern: And so academic IS has to find some way of accommodating to, and distinguishing itself from, IT/ICT, at the same time trying to justify a specialist claim to that very technology.

To reiterate the point in terms of Communities of Practice introduced earlier, the various CoPs can be taken to represent sub-groups within the various parent disciplines alluded to by Ives et al. Historically speaking, some CoPs have disappeared or severely contracted, others have emerged from the dialogue as for-the-moment fully-fledged disciplines.

An example of the problems of external recognition and demarcation can be found in the announcement in late 2004 of the format of the Research Assessment Exercise (RAE) in the UK, scheduled for 2008. Without going into the intricate details of the project, the RAE is an accounting and auditing exercise that has taken place every few years across the higher education sector in the UK since the early 1990s. The results of the exercise are to grade each 'unit' within a university in terms of its research performance over the previous period – usually 5-7 years. Some universities submit a return to only a few units, with only a small proportion of their staff classed as 'research active'; others submit a significant proportion of their staff, and rely on the grading for a substantial portion of their research-related income. The exercise is anything but cosmetic. Universities sometimes seek to maximize their grading by luring research active staff from other institutions; and there is a danger that, like the richest teams in the English Premier League, some institutions will engage the best researchers that money can buy in order to maximize their RAE outcome.

One of the key contentious issues is the way in which the exercise is managed. The over-arching strategy is that research is peer-reviewed – with all the problems associated with this method. Thus researchers have to submit their work to a subject group of their 'peers'. In some subjects the name and extent of the group may not be too much of a problem – even though there will always be issues of personnel and selection criteria. But for many subjects the name and extent of the group are themselves major points of contention, and the announcement in late 2004 for the next RAE, and its slicing of the disciplinary pie have come under intense – but probably ineffectual – criticism from many academic sources. The following summary of the discussion among the e-mail based Conference of Heads & Professors of Computing is an indicative example.

This email outlines the options we have considered and our current proposal (i) "a separate "Informatics" panel to include UoAs 25, 26, 41 and maybe others". This solution recognises that CS/Informatics is *sui generis*, rather than a kind of maths, engineering or physical science and has had strong support from UKCRC and CPHC.

Other solutions, putting CS with maths, engineering or physical sciences, seem to introduce unnecessary bias. ... So it seems that UoAs 26 would not be interested in joining a new panel.

UKCRC had similar discussions with UoA 41 Library and Information Studies. They are reasonably happy where they are in Panel J and would not want to shift to be with us. ... So this option in this form won't fly. (but see below)

(ii) UoA 25 joins Panel G (Engineering subjects)

However it seems that pragmatically there might be difficulties in asking to join Panel G and simultaneously requesting to be excused use of their long established joint framework.

(iii) UoA 25 follows HEFCEs proposal – Panel F (Computer Science and Mathematics subjects)

... UKCRC came to the slightly reluctant conclusion that this is the least bad feasible option.

(iv) UKCRC proposes to respond in the following terms:

A – a robustly argued bullish proposal that we have a separate new panel with just one subpanel – UoA 25, Computer Science. Justification being that CS is different, evolving very fast, much interdisciplinarity ..., large number of submissions, represented in nearly every UK University of enormous significance for UK economy and industry etc etc, and that doing things any other way would be to damage the discipline for the sake of bureaucratic tidyness.

B – an implied or explicit fallback position of Panel F as they suggest – with the caveat that maths and CS should be seen as cognate only in that they are foundational for many other areas of science, and have interaction with many other disciplines, rather than that they are closer to each other in *content* than they are to other subjects. ... (Ursula Martin)

From the above it can be seen that the problem of a fragmented adhocracy is not unique to academic IS, although Computer Science is clearly a member of the same family. Also it should be noted that the term *informatics* is itself now claimed by the Computer Science community; and is used in a very different way from that developed here. Developing Haraway's insights, the term involves something more than *computer science, computing & IT, software engineering* or *academic IS*. Informatics in the sense developed in this book is clearly pointing to an embryonic discipline trying to emerge and mature.

If sociology is a discipline flawed as discourse, continually pleading for its right to exist, and a place and space to exist; then informatics is its younger, weaker and more voluble sibling – or rather group of siblings that includes information systems, software engineering and computing. The protestations that greet anything that can be regarded as an attack on, or a probing of, the integrity or value of any of these sub-disciplines are evidence of a general uneasiness and lack of confidence. Moreover given the lack of anything approaching a consensus within the sub-disciplines themselves regarding the common core of the discipline – epitomized by the continually elusive and inconsistent use of terms such as IS and IT – there are a whole host of potential and indeed actual adversaries and usurpers. The IS community – collective chimera it may be – has in part developed in response to these provocations.

What we now have is a basis for informatics emerging from the debates about the identity crisis within academic IS. Academic IS emerged from a confluence of developments within existing disciplines, particularly computer science, computing, information science, library and information studies, systems, accounting, management and business studies; and, critically, as support for the actual practice of computer-based IS development.[67] As such academic IS might be viewed as a classic case of inter-disciplinarity; a new discipline evolving from and within the interstices of two or more existing disciplines; borrowing heavily from its variegated conceptual ancestries before gradually developing its own 'narrated reality at one end and the narrating reason at the other'.

But this was simply not the case with academic IS. To begin with there was always a tension between academic IS being an *inter*-discipline and it being an *extra*-discipline, subsuming some of its forebears, and making them into its constituents. This may also be a characteristic of other emerging inter-disciplines; but in addition what distinguishes academic IS are the twin impulsions of technological advance and market-led demand.

With regard to the former, it has always been an issue in academic IS that teachers and researchers have been chasing not only a moving target, but one that is constantly accelerating in unpredictable directions. Those of us who tried to

---

67 Frank Land has pointed out in a personal communication that some of his earliest papers were prepared not for academic journals or audiences but for *State of the Art Conferences* for practitioners; these being the primary forum for such issues in the late 1960s and early 1970s.

establish courses dealing with the internet and world wide web in the 1990s continually had to run to keep up – often changing content and direction in mid-course: Similarly for anyone who has taught courses on e-commerce, e-government and the like in the current decade. This acceleration is not constant, nor is it always in the same direction. New technologies appear on top of preceding 'revolutionary' ones, and older technologies are given new impetus. This leads to market-led demands for graduates with *appropriate* or *relevant* skills; although by the time the curriculum has been established, and the students have graduated, the demands have transformed. Hence the constant search for *relevance* amongst the IS academy.[68]

Academic IS is then influenced by its inter-disciplinary origins and extra-disciplinary claims: Its constitutive reliance on a highly unstable but prevailing economic and technological context; and its excessive market-sensitivity. To date this has led to three key results, all premised on growth: Growth in resources, growth in technological range and scope; growth in conceptual reach and ambit.

The growth in resources has been directly market-led. There has been an insatiable demand for ICT-skilled graduates – covering everything from basic computer skills to major systems and network management and development, and including software development and programming – and since the 1990s expanding to include web-development and internet skills. This has fuelled a steady growth in demand for undergraduate programmes in IT, ICT, computing, IS and the like. Consequently there has been an increase in academic posts for teachers and researchers, with funding, publications, etc., and the establishment of specific departments within universities. (Although it must be noted that this has been remarkably inconsistent, with some specific IS departments being established, but in other cases IS-type activities have developed within

---

68 A glance at the numerous reports on curriculum development, bodies of knowledge, links to professional practice readily attests to this – see FRISCO, IMBOK, PMBOK, IS2002, etc.

departments or faculties of Computing, IT, Applied Social Studies, Business & Management, or even Informatics.)

Ives et al rightly point out that 'the importance of the IS field in academia has rested on the market demand for skilled IS professionals'. Consequently any diminution in that demand will provoke a crisis in the academy, and will be a key contributory factor in any 'crisis of identity'.

Growth in technological range and scope has developed in parallel with the growth in resources. Indeed as one set of demands nears a level of equilibrium with supply, another set arises as the technology develops or changes. The emergence of the computer as a commercially useful and feasible tool in the form of mainframe machines in the 1950s provoked demand for certain skills; but this demand grew beyond all expectations once the personal computer was an affordable commodity both at home and at work. The demand for these skills was then supplemented with demands for skills with the development and implementation of communications technology – from IT to ICT. Then came the advent of the internet as a commercial reality with all that this implied – demands for web-designers, web-site hosting and so on. It may be that this pace cannot be maintained indefinitely, and in the medium to long term, lack of physical resources combined with massive climate change will probably mark an end-point of some sort (as it seems to have done with the sharp decline in demand for such courses in the middle of the first decade of the 21st century); but in the short to medium term, following the logic of Ellul's arguments, this incessant flow will not cease. Indeed as Howard Rheingold has argued in a recent book (2003), the internet itself is only in its infancy, and the most profound developments are still to come as technologies of mobile computing, communications and the internet combine to offer cheap and accessible wireless internet access to all – or at least to significant proportions of 'all'.

The third form of growth refers to the ways in which computer and communications technologies have become ubiquitous. This is not just in the sense that computers are everywhere available for use; but far more importantly because the computer metaphor has become a potently defining one. The workings of the brain, human cognition, social processes, organizations and entire societies are likened to computers. As computer technology develops and increases in power, its protagonists claim ever greater application of computation and computer modelling so that all manner of problems can be 'solved' using this technology. Combining these two facets of ubiquity produces a situation where the computer is no longer a specialized and remote technology, associated with a specialized and remote discipline protected from other disciplinary interests by a general lack of access to the concepts and the technical resources. On the contrary, the entire operation of computer and communications technology is now of central interest to a whole range of contending disciplinary discourses; including business and management, social sciences, cultural studies, and philosophy. Each of these may view the issues and substance of the narrated reality in a distinct and different manner, but the overall impact on the IS academy and computing is one of being under attack, or, in Markus' terms having the disciplinary turf hauled away.

Generally the period from the 1950s to the present has been a perfect demonstration of Ellul's ideas about technology in general, and computers in particular. In Weizenbaum's words it was a technology 'waiting to be discovered'; moreover the 'remaking of the world in the image of the computer started long before there were any electronic computers' (1984).

What we have in this period from the 1950s to the early 21st century is the unprecedented emergence and growth of the paradigmatic liquid discipline; informatics. The narrated reality and the narrated reason have developed in tandem, so that what at first was a technical reality, with a technical form of reason, has now become a dominant aspect of social reality. A key feature of this new and inchoate reality is that it is *praxeomorphic*; human capabilities, social phenomena and even the natural world are embraced conceptually within the terms of ICT: Hence the importance of articulating a rigorous and all-encompassing programme of informatics.

The discipline has been indelibly marked as crisis-ridden from the start, but in the past decade or so this crisis has taken on new forms linked to the three aspects of growth discussed previously; and the ways in which the context and impetus behind these three aspects have changed.

With regard to the first aspect – resources – the situation is that the previously ever-expanding demand for skills and practitioners has now levelled-off and even started to decline; in some cases the decline is marked and rapid. This has reawakened the call for 'relevance', but still begs the questions 'relevant to whom or to what?' The usual response, and indeed a guiding principle of many discussions on IS curricula and development as academic discipline, is that it must be relevant to employers and so linked to employment opportunities for IS graduates. Recent debates both in the US and Europe have centred on how the curriculum can be tuned to employers' needs and to the employment prospects of graduates. Yet this is to misunderstand what is happening in the liquid modern world. First it must be understood that education has become commodified just as Lyotard argued (1984). Across the entire higher education sector – particularly in the developed world – there is a decreasing demand for degree courses in physics, maths, and chemistry – chemistry is virtually extinct in UK universities, apart from a few centres of excellence. So the predicted demise of academic IS is not an isolated instance. Student demand is for courses in 'vocational' – i.e. marketable – subjects such as law and accountancy, but also new arrivals like web-design and entrepreneurship; although non-marketable ones, such as history, English, and arts and humanities in general, continue to recruit students. With the increasing trend to outsourcing, off-shoring – or whatever it is called when employment opportunities move from expensive to cheap sources of labour and skill – many other disciplines, both well-established and newly emerging, will fall prey to the vagaries of the market. The current decline in academic IS should, therefore, be seen as part of a general trend.

Moreover trying to chase the market will not work. Some of the debates on the IS curriculum continue to hold out the lure of 'relevance' and practice-oriented goals; but this is to mistake the changing nature of education in liquid modernity. The concept of education as a process that ended, for most people, in their late teens or early twenties, belongs to a more solid era when the concept of a career and an associated identity were equally grounded in solid expectations. People now have to be 'flexible', and so education needs to become a service to be bought in stages during one's lifetime, as one proceeds continuously to recreate one's identity. Gone are the days of the concept of a single life-long career; or a life-time of employment with one paternalistic employer. Again as Bauman has pointed out, in the old days of solid modernity the factory owner needed the employees (almost) as much as the employees needed the factory owner; but now the owner can and does simply up-sticks and move the factory elsewhere. Mannheim may or may not have been correct to see intellectuals as 'free-floating' in the 1950s, but by the first decade of the 21st century the real free-floaters are the capitalists.

With regard to education there is an incessant move towards ever greater commodification and packaging of education; and this impacts particularly on its mode and forms of delivery – at-a-distance, on-line, e-learning, digital diploma mills, etc.[69] Whatever one's perspective or hopes/fears at this prospect, the lessons for curriculum design are clear; the role of the educators – of the academy – is not one of selling a single package to someone once-and-for-all, neither is it simply equipping someone for the long journey through life. Education needs to become more akin to a doctor-patient relationship. Students think they know what they want; but they may be wrong. In any case, even if they are right, they will only be right for a short period of time. So gearing up for a curriculum that will simply bring in the students today is of only limited use.

Similarly there is no point meeting the requirements of employers or of the market in general. The employers will most likely either have disappeared by the time the students graduate, or will have found cheaper and more amenable sources

---

69 See particularly the work of David Noble, 1998

of skills and labour elsewhere.[70] If we are to start planning with regard to the future of the educated workforce then we need to pay at least as much attention to Vonnegut's *Player Piano* – where most of the population are uneducated and unemployed, literally consigned to the waste-lands and scrap-heaps of society – as to any government white paper or EU document extolling the knowledge society. If we really lived in a knowledge society then teaching would be the hardest profession to enter and the best paid. Moreover one must be severely sceptical about predictions for future employment needs; what happened to the predictions from the 1970s that by 2010 we would all need to be programmers? Or earlier ones about running out of suitably trained telephone switchboard operators or chauffeurs?

The second form of growth, in technological range and scope, might be thought of as countering the decline resulting from the demise of the first form. But this would be to equate technological advance with market demand for IS graduates. There is certainly continued and marked technological innovation, but as both Ellul and Castells have argued, this innovation feeds on itself and so requires diminishing input from outside; the innovations serve as the basis for future innovations. Moreover the market takes on a guiding and constituting role, so that skills are developed where they are cheaper to sustain – software, like sports shoes, is now a prime export from Asia. To an extent growth of this form does propel growth in the first sense, since courses and curricula extend accordingly. Anyone casting their eye over courses on offer in schools or departments of computing, IS, informatics, systems or the like, will find no shortage of topics from across the sciences and arts and humanities. We can lay claim to the disciplinary turf of our neighbours as well as the next guys.

---

70 The current position in many countries is that education is seen as a commodity consumed as an individual good, with students taking on the guise of customers. The marketing of education in this way may not lead to the end of history, but in the UK it is in danger of leading to the end of chemistry and maths.

The third form concerns the ways in which computer and communications technologies have become ubiquitous; with the metaphorical imagery of ICT and its associated features now transformed from a technical peculiarity to part of our *common sense*. This very ubiquity offers both threats and opportunities each inevitably accompanied by issues of dissipation and contestation. In chapter 1 Markus' admonition about the possible disappearance of 'Academic IS' was mentioned; together with her equivocal conclusion. Her argument can be seen as one example of the dilemma that informatics itself has to face; to seek an established base as a discipline in its own right, or to try to accomplish some sustainable beachhead within other disciplines. She offers a shorthand characterization of the discipline of 'Academic IS' as the 'electronic integration of socio-economic activity'; our definition of informatics might be evoked as *the socio-economic evocation of electronic activity*. It can, I trust, be agreed that the issues encompassed by informatics are important; but where in the academy will these be developed? In the light of Carr's (2003) article it might be averred by some that 'IT Doesn't Matter', but informatics certainly does.

In the immediate aftermath of the publication of the paper by Benbasat & Zmud (discussed in chapter 1) the Association of Information Systems [AIS], specifically in the guise of its two key on-line publications[71], hosted a wide-ranging debate on the topic of the nature and focus of the IS discipline. Naturally no consensus was reached, but the entire exercise demonstrated the variety of views amongst those who sought to identify themselves as part of the IS discipline. A similarly intense range of retorts was evoked in response to the publication Carr's article in the Harvard Business Review. In both cases the process of responding in itself was clearly the key benefit.

A lesson to be drawn from these episodes is the wide range of possible points of weakness that informatics displays if there is any attempt to develop it as

---

71 *JAIS* and *CAIS*, respectively *Journal/Communications of the Association of Information Systems*

a hermetically-sealed discipline. Like an over-stuffed suitcase, securing one side merely exposes the breaches and ruptures elsewhere. But this should not be taken to mean that the subject matter of informatics is of no importance: On the contrary, precisely because of its importance, any attempt to stake an exclusive and excluding disciplinary claim will be seen as a threat to other, more established, and slightly less flawed and contrite fields. Moreover the critical issues encompassed by informatics render the establishment of an informatics discourse a crucial endeavour – however transitory or imperfect. Staking disciplinary claims is both necessary and self-defeating.

The magnitude and significance of the issues encompassed by the definition of informatics used makes it paramount that a disciplinary space be established and sustained, even though this space differs markedly both from what the current IS academy, and the range of theorists and specifiers of the information society envisage. The flawed discourse of informatics must take on the challenge of becoming still more flawed at least in the sense of becoming more disorganized and more extensive.

In chapter 1 Bauman's pithy description of the originating motivation behind sociology was rephrased to apply to informatics – even if it applied most obviously to a specifically technicist understanding of IS and informatics; 'brought into being by the encounter between the awesome task of the management of organizational processes on a grand, *corporate and* societal scale and the ambitions of the modern state *and corporation'*. This highly paradoxical encounter evoked a range of responses, and is at the root of the continuing debates over the 'relevance' of IS. Many of these debates derive from a position that presumes a dichotomy between 'academics' and 'practitioners'. This dichotomy is often stated in knowingly stereotypical terms; thus academics are seen, disparagingly, as continually arguing about the meaning of concepts such as *information*; while practitioners actually get on with developing and managing information systems. Hence academic IS fails the test of relevance, since it is of no immediate use to practitioners; indeed for many there is the worry that it may

be of no use at all. A recent posting on the ISWORLD list by one of the founding
fathers of IS threw down a challenge to the academic community as follows

> A feature of the IS academic community is that it has not
> itself initiated new uses of IS. We note that the IS
> community is very good at scrambling aboard the latest
> bandwagon, as often engaging in the hype rather than being
> properly critical. The list of bandwagons which the IS
> community has adopted is long. Yesterday it was BPR, then
> Knowledge Management, ERP and perhaps the current fad is
> mobile computing.
>
> Each bandwagon spawns conferences, journals and new
> texts. Much of the work is revealing and helps to broaden the
> understanding of students and practitioners. But too much is
> shallow and engages in rhetoric rather than analysis. Few of
> the bandwagons survive more than a few years.
>
> Where is the work in our community which yields new ideas
> on how IS can serve mankind?
>
> Am I being unfair?' (Frank Land, 2004)

Or in other words, to borrow from Monty Python's *Life of Brian*; 'What
have the IS academics ever done for (IS) us?' Unfortunately the response is not
even remotely similar to the one provided in the film.[72] Although if we replace
'IS' with 'ICT' then perhaps we do get something akin to the *Life of Brian*
example; massive databases, speedy and low-cost communication with specific
individuals, groups and colleagues, new forms of broadcasting and sharing, new

---

72 Reg – 'All right, but apart from the sanitation, the medicine, education, wine, public order,
irrigation, roads, a fresh water system, and public health, what have the Romans ever done for us?'

potential for learning and teaching, new forms of immediacy in interaction and consumption.

On the other hand there are those who look upon ICT – and by implication at currently existing academic IS – as peculiarly relevant to the existing political-economic order; its relevance being that it is the handmaid of advanced, global capitalism. So far from failing the test of serving humanity, IS – as an inextricable component of technicist ICT – is seen by many as a critical part of the new mode of exploitation; some, including Weizenbaum, might even see it as the dominant component. And there is a great deal of evidence in *MISQ, ISR* and on the ISWORLD website to support both Land's points about bandwagons and the criticisms linking the discipline with globalized capital.

The current debates about IS curricula offer further indications. There is the realization that the areas encompassed by computing and information systems have expanded both in the sense that their subject matter now incorporates issues well beyond the confines of the narrowly technical, and in the sense that the content of their subject matter now involves the sort of ubiquity alluded to by Markus (as discussed in chapter 1). The introductory remarks in the fairly recent curriculum reports on undergraduate and postgraduate curricula reflect this. Thus the 2002 report notes that

> All aspects of the computing field are facing rapid, continuous change. As a result, university-level Information Systems (IS) curricula need frequent updating to remain effective. Since most academic units have mechanisms to maintain currency of curricula, what is the role of professional society curriculum committees? If an IS academic unit were providing graduates solely to local business and government, the input on program contents could be derived from representatives of local organizations that hire the graduates. However, local employment is not the sole objective for undergraduate majors in Information Systems. Students from IS programs accept jobs in widely dispersed geographic areas.

Therefore, the availability of curriculum models enables local academic units to maintain academic programs that are consistent both with regional and national employment needs and with the common body of knowledge of the IS field.

The Postgraduate equivalent makes a similar point

The model curriculum is designed to serve as a set of standards upon which individual schools can base their curriculum. It is compatible with MS programs ranging from 30 to 60 or more units offered in a variety of locations in the university, including business schools, schools of information systems, computer science departments, and liberal arts schools. By adopting this curriculum, faculty, students, and employers can be assured that MS graduates are competent in a set of professional knowledge and skills, know about a particular field in detail from the career track, and are instilled with a strong set of values essential for success in the Information Systems field. In short, it is a program that reflects current and future industry needs.[73]

The curriculum documents are lengthy and detailed, and it would be far too simple to summarize them as simply training guides for key technical apparatchiks for the employment needs of informational capitalism; but the tendency is clearly slanted to the globalized employment demands of contemporary capitalism. An indication of this is the very recent realization that IT/IS graduates from North American and Western European universities are expensive commodities, far too expensive for leaner-and-fitter, pared-to-the-bone international organizations with the ability to outsource and off-shore many of

---

73 Both reports are available at http://www.aisnet.org/Curriculum/

184

their IT/IS operations and procedures. The consequent drop in demand for such graduates has led to a similar fall in demand for undergraduate and graduate places on associated courses, and hence a massive re-evaluation of the curriculum even since the 2002 version mentioned earlier. (At the time of writing a similar trend is occurring in Northern Europe – although there are perhaps other factors involved in the decline.)

In fact there has always been a high level of contestation within the IS academy, and these recent developments have merely strengthened the more critical or *abnormal discourses*. Groups such as IFIP WG8.2[74] have sustained a high level of debate on topics that extend well beyond the confines of the IS discipline as evoked by the disciplinary and curricula policing of the IS academy – and many of the most expansive responses to Benbasat & Zmud came from members of this group. Yet an indication of the imbalance between the abnormal and the normal discourses would be the enormous weight of research, publications, curricula activities, conferences etc which unquestioningly assume that the world is technically-oriented, consumer-led and largely on-line; and that the trickle-down model of wealth creation and division is 'good enough' to preclude any efforts at redistribution.

Those seeking to counter this view have to take issue with the usually taken-for-granted, and therefore un-stated, often sophomoric sociology rather than with the technology itself: Hence the importance of introducing a wide readership to Bauman's work to provide an alternative backdrop for the development of such discourses. This can help foster the work that has already started to engage with the continuing critique of the technical and technicist. What is required, however, is a truly trans-disciplinary movement that seeks to develop an 'incessant activity of discourse ... spawn[ing] the narrated reality at one end and the narrating reason at the other'.

---

74 see http://www.ifipwg82.org/tiki-index.php

In order to encourage such consciously proto-disciplinary activities people need an idea of what is involved in 'thinking informatically'; to borrow and adapt another of Bauman's phrases. We have to begin to understand the specific nature of the 'biological, social, linguistic and cultural changes' to which our attention is drawn as the source, nature and limitations of technicism and the full extent and complexities of informatics become apparent. This demands that we have to make a start on conceiving society in terms that move beyond the confines and misconceptions of the modernist and mechanist views that are all too common across all disciplines.

Haraway's definition is open ended enough to encourage and promote the development of a discipline perhaps devoid of a centre but with many peripheries. The expanded definition of informatics may at least serve as something around which the like-minded can huddle for warmth if not for protection from the outside. There is at present no outside, the boundaries of informatics are best conceived of as a disciplinary Klein bottle. As the discussions of the terms *information, communication(s)*, and *technology* indicate, attempts to anchor the fragmented adhocracy around clear definitions of the central and defining terms at the heart of IS/ICT – even if the informatics mantle is not accepted – are founded on profound misconceptions or partial understandings of the terms themselves. Information is not a 'mystical fluid' distilled from raw data: Communication is not a process of flow from active transmitter to passive receiver: Technology is not an off-limits, asocial form of magic that drives society along once it is widely used. Informatics has a profound and promising basis, but only once each of these three terms – and the collective one of ICT – are seen as essentially contested and profoundly social. Currently much our thinking is improperly wedded to inappropriate and disabling metaphors and technicist trappings. Moreover, to echo another of Bauman's points, the *discipline* of informatics is constituted by these essential contestations and not by any final resting place and set of agreed conclusions, which would actually signal its place of interment.

It might be thought possible that despite the essentially social character of informatics an argument could be made for the IS academy to build its disciplinary boundaries without recourse to the full range of our definition. After all there are specific issues and complexities concerned with the technology – hardware, software, communications, etc. This is a reasonable position for some, and indeed the arguments of those such as Benbasat & Zmud, and Orlikowski & Iacono might be interpreted as attempts to anchor the discipline around the, mostly tangible, technology. But the responses to successive efforts at disciplinary characterization indicate that for many others within the IS academy this option is simply not available or plausible; neither is it desirable. The IS discipline is replete with affectations of the social and sociological as well as the technical or technological. Any boundary building efforts will be undermined by these insiders continually and insistently ready and willing to extend their reach beyond limiting concepts such as the 'IT-artefact', 'nomological net', or whatever other conceptual anchorage is on offer. The far-reaching scope of informatics has always been present within the IS academy. Now it is high time for it to emerge in its own right.

BIBLIOGRAPHY

Alexander J. & Smith, P.; 'The Strong Programme in Cultural Sociology'; in Alexander J.; *The Meanings of Social Life: A Cultural Sociology*; OUP; 2003

Angell, I.; *The New Barbarian Manifesto: How to Survive the Information Age*; Kogan Page; 2000

Ashby W.R.; *Design for a Brain*; Chapman & Hall; 1959

Avgerou C., Ciborra C. & Land F.; *The Social Study of Information and Communication Technology: Innovation, Actors, and Contexts*, OUP; 2004

Bangemann; *Bangemann Report, Europe and the Global Information Society*; available at http://www.cyber-rights.org/documents/bangemann.htm; 1994

Bauman Z.; *Towards a Critical Sociology*; Routledge; 1976

———; *Legislators and Interpreters*; Polity; 1987

———; 'The Changing Discursive Formation of Sociology'; in *Intimations of Post Modernity*; Routledge; 1992

———; 'Is there a Postmodern Sociology?'; in *Intimations of Postmodernity*; Routledge; 1992

———; *Postmodern Ethics*, Blackwell; 1993

———; *Globalization*; Polity; 1998

———; *Culture as Praxis*; SAGE, orig 1973; Routledge; 1999

———; *In Search of Politics*; Polity; 1999

———; *Liquid Modernity*; Polity; 2000

———; *Community*; Polity; 2001

———; *Society under Siege*; Polity; 2002

———; *Wasted Lives*; Polity; 2004

Bauman Z. & May T.; *Thinking Sociologically*; Blackwell; 2001

Beck U.; *What Is Globalization?*; Polity; 1999

Beck U. & Beck-Gernsheim E.; *Individualization: Institutionalized Individualism and Its Social and Political Consequences*; SAGE; 2001

Beer S.; *The Brain of the Firm: Managerial Cybernetics of Organization*; Allen Lane; 1981

Bell D.; *The End of Ideology*; Free Press; 1961

——; *The Coming of Post-Industrial Society*; Basic Books; 1976

——; 'The Information Society', in Forester T.; (ed); pp500-549; 1979

Benbasat I. & Zmud R.W.; 'The Identity Crisis within the IS Discipline: Defining and Communicating the Discipline's Core Properties'; *MIS Quarterly*, (27) 2, pp. 183-194; 2003

Berman B.; 'The Computer Metaphor: Bureaucratizing the Mind'; *Science as Culture* 7; 1989

Berry D.M. & Lawrence B.; guest editors' introduction on 'Requirements Engineering', *IEEE Software*; March/April 1998

Bertalanffy L. von; *General Systems Theory*; George Braziller; 1969

Black M.; 'More about Metaphor'; in Ortony; 1993

Boland R.J.; 'The In-formation of Information systems'; in Boland R.J. & Hirschheim R.A.; *Critical Issues in Information Systems Research*; Wiley; 1987

Bryant A.; '"It's Engineering Jim; but not as we know it": Software Engineering, solution to the software crisis or part of the problem?', *ICSE 2000*, Limerick, June 2000

——; 'Knowledge Management – the Ethics of the Agora or the Mechanisms of the Market?', paper presented at *HICSS*, Hawaii, 2006

Bryant A., Bauman Z., Metzger G. & Pollock G.; 'Liquid Arts – A Symposium', schedule to appear in *Theory, Culture & Society*, 2006/7

Carr N.; 'IT Doesn't Matter'; *Harvard Business Review*; May 2003

——; *Does IT Matter?*; HBS Press; 2004

Carroll L.; *Through the Looking Glass*; Penguin; 1994

Castells M.; *The Rise of the Network Society; The Information Age – Volume 1*; Blackwell; 1996

Castells M.; *The Power of Identity: The Information Age – Volume 2*; Blackwell; 2003

Castells M.; *End of Millenium: The Information Age – Volume 3*; Blackwell; 2000

Churchman C.W.; *The Systems Approach*, Dell; 1984

Cringley R.; *Accidental Empires*; Viking; 1992

Curtis G. & Cobham D.; *Business Information Systems*; 4th edition, FT/Pitmans; 2002

Davenport T.H. & Prusak L.; *Working Knowledge: How Organizations Manage What They Know*; Harvard Business School Press; 1997

Davis A.; 'The Harmony in Rechoirments'; editorial in *IEEE Software*; March/April 1998 – see Berry and Lawrence; 1998

Dick P.K.; *We Can Remember It For You Wholesale (The Collected Short Stories of Philip K. Dick)*; Gollancz; 2000

——; *Do Androids Dream of Electric Sheep?*; Gollancz; 2004

Douglas M.; *Purity and Danger: An Analysis of Concepts of Pollution and Taboo*; Routledge; 2002

Drucker, P.; *The Essential Drucker: The Best of Sixty Years of Peter Drucker's Essential Writings on Management*; Harper Collins; 2003

Ehrenreich, B.; *Nickel and Dimed*; Holt; 2001

Ellul J.; *The Technological System*; Continuum; 1980

Emery F.E. & Trist E.L.; 'The causal texture of organizational environments'; *Human Relations,* vol.18 (1965), pp. 21-32; 1965

Ferry G.; *A Computer Called LEO*; Fourth Estate; 2003

Feyerabend P; *Against Method: Outline of an Anarchistic Theory of Knowledge*; Verso; 1993

Forester T., (ed); *The Microelectronics Revolution*; Blackwell; 1980

FRISCO report; 'A Framework for Information Systems Concepts'; available at http://www.liacs.nl/~verrynst/frisco.html; 2001

Galbraith J.K.; 'The Unfinished Business of the Century'; lecture given at LSE
June; 1999

Gallie W.B.; 'Essentially Contested Concepts'; *Proceedings of the Aristotelian
Society*; 167; 1956

Gibson W.; *Neuromancer*; Voyager; 1995

Gibson W. & Sterling B.; *The Difference Engine*; Gollancz; 1996

Giddens A.; *The Constitution of Society: Outline of the Theory of Structuration*;
Polity; 1984

Giddens A.: *Runaway World*; Reith Lectures; 1999; available at
http://news.bbc.co.uk/hi/english/static/events/reith_99/default.htm

Gleick J.; *Chaos*; Vintage; 1988

———; 'Chaos', available at
http://www.chaosmatrix.org/library/chaos/science/bstchaos.html; nd

Gould S.J.; *Panda's Thumb*; Penguin; 1990

Habermas, J.; *Knowledge and Human Interests*; Heinemann; 1972

Haraway D.; 'A Manifesto for Cyborgs: Science, Technology, and Socialist
Feminism in the 1980s'; *Socialist Review*; 80, 65-108; 1985

Hayles N.K.; *How We Became Posthuman: Virtual Bodies in Cybernetics,
Literature and Informatics*; Univ of Chicago Press; 1999

Held D. & McGrew A.; *The Global Transformations Reader: An Introduction to
the Globalization Debate*; Polity; 2003

Hirst P. & Thompson G.; *Globalization in Question: The International Economy
and the Possibilities of Governance*; Polity; 1999

Illich I.; *Limits to Medicine: Medical Nemesis – The Expropriation of Health*,
Marion Boyars; 2001

IMBOK; *Information Management Body of Knowledge*; available at
http://www.imbok.org/pag_home.htm; nd

Introna L.; *Management, Information and Power*; Macmillan; 1997

IS2002; *IS2002 website*,

    http://192.245.222.212:8009/IS2002Doc/Main_Frame.htm; 2002

Ives B., Parks M.S., Porra, J. & Silva, L.; 'Phylogeny and Power in the IS

    Domain: A Response to Benbasat and Zmud's Call for Returning to the IT

    Artifact'; *JAIS*; vol 5(3), available at

    http://jais.isworld.org/articles/default.asp?vol=5&art=4; 2004

Kafka F.; 'My Destination'; available at www.kafka.org, nd

Kauffman S.; *Investigations*; OUP; 2000

Kotter, J.;

Lakoff G. & Johnson M.; *Metaphors We Live By*; University of Chicago Press;

    1981

Lamb R. & Kling R.; 'Reconceptualizing Users as Social Actors in IS Research';

    MISQ, vol 27 (2), pp197-235; 2003

Larsen S.; 'The WSIS; whose freedom, whose information?'; *Open Democracy*

    http://opendemocracy.net/content/articles/PDF/1630.pdf; 2003

Latour B.; *Science in Action*; Open University Press; 1987

Laudon K. & Laudon J.; *Management Information Systems*; 7th edition, Prentice

    Hall; 2002

Lave J. & Wenger E.; *Situated Learning: Legitimate Peripheral Participation*;

    CUP; 1991

Liebenau J. & Backhouse J.; *Understanding Information: An Introduction*;

    Macmillan; 1990

Lienhard J.H.; 'The Butterfly Effect'; available on *The Engines of Our Ingenuity*

    web site, http://www.uh.edu/engines/epi652.htm; nd

Long L. & Long N.; *Computers*; 8th edition, Prentice Hall; 2001

Lyotard J-F.; *The Postmodern Condition: A Report on Knowledge*; Manchester

    University Press (French original 1979); 1984

Mandelbrot B.B. & Hudson R.L.; *The (Mis)Behaviour of Markets*; Profile; 2004

Markus L; 'Thinking the Unthinkable: What Happens if the IS Field as we Know it Goes Away?'; in Currie W.L. & Galliers R. (eds); *Rethinking Management Information Systems*; Oxford; 1999

Mason R.; 'Putting *Systems* Back into Management Information Systems'; paper delivered at the Gordon Davis Symposium; May, 2005

Masuda Y.; Information Society as Post-industrial Society; Transaction; 1982

McKeown P.; *IT & The Networked Economy*; 2nd edition, Thompson; 2003

Mills, C. W.; *The Sociological Imagination*; Oxford University Press; 1959

Mintzberg, H.; *Mintzberg on Management*; Free Press; 1989

Mowshowitz A.; 'On Approaches to the Study of Social Issues in Computing', *Communications of the ACM*; 24(3); 1981

Naisbitt J.; *Megatrends: Ten New Directions Transforming Our Lives*; Warner; 1982

Negroponte N.; *Being Digital*; Vintage; 1995

Noble D.; *Digital Diploma Mills*; Part 1 available at http://www.firstmonday.org/issues/issue3_1/noble/; 1998

Nolan R.L.; *Managing the Data Resource Function*; 2nd edition, West; 1982

O'Brien J.; *Introduction to Information Systems*; 11th edition, McGraw Hill; 2003

O'Leary T. & O'Leary L.; *Computing Essentials 1999-2000*; Irwin; 1999

Orlikowski W.J. & Iacono C.S.; 'Desperately Seeking the *IT* in IT research – A Call to Theorizing the IT Artifact'; *Information Systems Research*, (12) 2, pp. 121-134; 2001

Ortony A. (ed); *Metaphor and Thought*; 2nd edition, Cambridge; 1993

Phua K.L.; *Veblen's Singapore*; available at http://phuakl.tripod.com/eTHOUGHT/Veblen.html; nd

PMBOK; *Project Management Body of Knowledge*, available at http://www.projectsmart.co.uk/pmbok.html; nd

Pollock G.F.S.; *Differencing the Canon: Feminism and the Writing of Arts Histories*; Routledge; 1999

Prigogine I.; *The End of Certainty*; Free Press; 1996

Raymond E.S.; *The Cathedral and the Bazaar*; O'Reilly; 2001

Reddy M.; 'The conduit metaphor: A case of frame conflict in our language about language'; in Ortony, 1993

Rheingold H.; *Smart Mobs: The Next Social Revolution*; Perseus; 2003

Roszak T.; *The Cult of Information: Neo-Luddite Treatise on High-tech, Artificial Intelligence and the True Art of Thinking*; Pantheon; 1986

Schön D.; 'Generative Metaphor: A perspective on problem setting in social policy'; in Ortony, 1993

Sennett R.; *The Corrosion of Character: Personal Consequences of Work in the New Capitalism*; W W Norton; 2000

Sennett R. & Cobb J.; *The Hidden Injuries of Class*; CUP; 1977

Shannon C.; 'The Mathematical Theory of Communication'; *Bell Systems Techncial Journal*, vol 27; available from http://cm.bell-labs.com/cm/ms/what/shannonday/shannon1948.pdf; 1948

Shannon, C. & Weaver W.; *The Mathematical Theory of Communication*; Univ. of Illinois Press; 1959

Sommerville I.; *Software Engineering*; 5th edition, Addison-Wesley; 1996

Stewart S.; 'The Complexity Complex'; *University of Chicago Magazine,* Volume 95, Issue 2; 2002

Stiglitz J.; *The Roaring Nineties: Why We're Paying the Price for the Greediest Decade in History*; Penguin; 2004

Sveiby K-E.; 'What is Information'; available at http://www.sveiby.com/articles/Information.html#contradiction; 1998

Toffler A.; *Future Shock*, Pan; 1973

Turban E., McLean E. & Wetherbe J.; *IT for Management*; 2nd edition, Wiley; 2001

Usher M.J.; *Information Theory for Information Technologists*; Macmillan; 1984

Vonnegut K.; *Player Piano*; Bantam (orig 1952); 1999

Webster F. (ed); *The Information Society Reader*; Routledge; 2004

—— (ed); *Theories of the Information Society*; 2nd edition, Routledge; 2002

194

Weizenbaum J; *Computer Power and Human Reason*; Penguin; 1984

——; 'Once More, the Computer Revolution'; in Forester, T., (ed), pp550-570; 1980

Westfall R.; 'An IS Research Relevance Manifesto', available at http://www.cyberg8t.com/westfalr/relevant.html; 1997; a revised version – 1999 – is available at http://www.csupomona.edu/~rdwestfall/ais/relevancymanifesto.html

Wiener N.; *Cybernetics*; MIT Technology Press; 1948

Williams R.; *Television: Technology and Cultural Form*; Fontana; 1974

——; *Communications*; 3rd edition, Penguin; 1976

——; *Keywords: A Vocabulary of Culture and Society*; Fontana; 1976

Winner L.; *The Whale and The Reactor*; University of Chicago Press; 1986

Winston B.; *Media, Technology and Society: A History – From the Printing Press to the Superhighway*; Routledge; 1998

WSIS; 'Declaration of Principles'; Document WSIS-03/GENEVA/DOC/4-E, available at http://www.itu.int/wsis/documents/doc_multi.asp?lang=en&id=1161|1160; 2003

WSIS Civil Society; 'Shaping Information Societies for Human Needs'; available at www.worldsummit2003.de/download_en/ WSIS-CS-Decl-08Dec2003-eng.rtf; 2003

Zorkocy P. & Heap N.; *Information Technology; an introduction*; 4th edition, Pitman; 2003

INDEX